# The Plants of Dr Bach

## Molecules, Remedies and Lore

Gwenda Kyd

Vervain Publishing

## Acknowledgements:

This publication would not have been possible without the efforts of many people and I would like to extend my thanks to everyone who contributed.

The book is loosely based on a series of blogs 'Secrets of the Bach Flower Remedy Plants' I published between 2015 and 2017. It was due to the feedback and encouragement I received from readers of the blogs that I decided to expand and adapt them into this publication. I'd like to thank Stefan Ball at the Bach Centre for sharing links to the posts with the Bach community and for his help and advice throughout the process. In addition, to all those who shared links or made encouraging comments – thanks!

Photos are a very important part of this book – how better to get to know the plants better than by looking at them? So, the contribution of the photographers who kindly contributed photographs – Mo Sibbons, Nicola Hanefeld, Kate Lennard-Jones, Frauke Möschler, Tracey van den Ban and contributors to Pixabay, Wikimedia Commons and other online depositories – is gratefully acknowledged.

Publishing a book isn't cheap and I'd like to thank those whose financial contributions made it possible. Finally, I'd like to thank my text-editing team – Mary Kyd, Mo Sibbons and Dr Seth Wiggin for their input and patience and Jo Ace who designed and typeset the book.

Published by Vervain Publishing, 39 Regatta Court, Oyster Row, Cambridge, CB5 8NS, UK

© 2018 Vervain Publishing

A catalogue record for this book is available from the British Library.
ISBN 978-0-9928998-1-3

Designed and typeset by Jo Ace

Printed in Great Britain by Latimer Trend & Co. Ltd., Plymouth

# Contents

Introduction                               iv

**Section 1**   Willow                     1

**Section 2**   Aspen                      6

**Section 3**   Pine                       9

**Section 4**   Horse Chestnuts            14

**Section 5**   Sweet Chestnut             19

**Section 6**   Walnut                     24

**Section 7**   Cherry Plum                27

**Section 8**   Crab Apple                 31

**Section 9**   Larch                      36

**Section 10**  Olive                      41

**Section 11**  Hornbeam                   45

**Section 12**  Oak                        50

**Section 13**  Beech                      56

**Section 14**  Holly                      61

**Section 15**  Elm                        67

**Section 16**  Heather                    72

**Section 17**  Wild Oat                   76

**Section 18**  Gorse                      81

**Section 19**  Vervain                    85

**Section 20**  Centaury                   89

**Section 21**  Gentian                    93

**Section 22**  Agrimony                   97

**Section 23**  Star of Bethlehem          101

**Section 24**  Clematis                   104

**Section 25**  Mustard                    108

**Section 26**  Chicory                    112

**Section 27**  Vine                       116

**Section 28**  Honeysuckle                121

**Section 29**  Wild Rose                  125

**Section 30**  Mimulus                    129

**Section 31**  Impatiens                  133

**Section 32**  Cerato                     136

**Section 33**  Scleranthus                139

**Section 34**  Rock Rose                  142

**Section 35**  Water Violet               146

**Section 36**  Rock Water                 149

Photo Credits                              152

# Introduction

The entrance to the Bach Centre, Oxfordshire

Dr Edward Bach (1886–1936) developed a system of healing using 38 flower essences made from 36 different plants. The Bach flower remedies are now known and used worldwide and many books have been written and are still being written offering insight into the remedies and how they can be used.

But what about the plants themselves? Dr Bach identified most growing in Wales and the south of England, looking for those with the correct energies to balance negative emotional states. He narrowed down his search by avoiding plants primarily used for food and those which he knew to be poisonous (like deadly nightshade and henbane) but he did consider those used in herbal remedies. Importantly, he used the essence of the flowers, where he believed the most powerful healing energy was found, and this differentiates his remedies from other plant-based remedies.[1]

But there's more to these plants than their flower essences or even their flowers. Like all other plants, they contain an array of chemical compounds which govern every aspect of their lives. Many are required for protection – plants don't have the ability to physically move away from danger like animals typically do, so they often defend themselves chemically.

Careful observation of plants can give us clues about what types of chemicals they contain. For example, leaves that are not attacked by fungi or bacteria probably incorporate antifungal and antibacterial compounds. Those avoided by herbivores are likely to have compounds which make them taste unpleasant and/or cause harm to the potential predator.

These chemical compounds lie at the root of many of the beneficial properties that plants possess. For example, oxidative stress has been linked to the effects of ageing and several conditions including hypertension, atherosclerosis and some cancers; antioxidants can reduce oxidative stress.[2] Plants'

**Common foxglove (*Digitalis purpurea*)**

protection against predators is particularly relevant as the same compounds produced to act on potential predators can also have an effect on us. For example, foxgloves protect themselves with compounds which cause a predator's heart rate to slow down. Eating too much of a foxglove plant will lead to death. However, the correct dose used in the correct way can be beneficial. Digitalis, or foxglove extract, has been used medicinally since the 13th century and compounds from digitalis including digoxin and digitoxin are still used to treat heart conditions today.

The medicinal properties of plants have been recognised for at least 60,000 years and even now plants still provide an important source of new drugs. In the 30 years prior to 2012, an estimated 50% of new drugs had their origin in the natural world, including plants.[3] And it's not just at a chemical level that plants can benefit our health. Recently, Japanese forest bathing (*shinrin yoku*) has become popular in the West. This involves simply taking leisurely walks in a forest. Among the benefits claimed are improved

immunity and sleep, reduced stress levels and blood pressure and increased energy and focus. How these benefits are achieved is unclear. One suggestion is that they may come from breathing phytoncides which trees produce for defence or it may be that simply spending time in a natural environment can uplift us.[4] Any contact at all with the natural world does seem to be beneficial. An experiment carried out on office-workers in Japan showed that even the presence of cut roses reduced stress.[5]

Plants also provide an important source of food. Most, or arguably all, our needs can be met by plants – as well as fruit and vegetables, there's grains, pulses, nuts and oils which together can provide a full range of nutrients.

And when you stop looking at plants only as a source of food or medicine or for their aesthetic beauty there is still a whole lot more they can teach us. Sometimes we've found ingenious ways of using ideas gleaned from plants. A well-known example is the development of Velcro. Swiss inventor Georges de Mestral (1907–90) got the idea for the hook and

**Greater burdock (*Articum lappa*)**

loop fastener after observing under a microscope the burs attached to his clothes and his dog's fur after a walk in the Alps. The hooks on the surface of the burs (thought to have been from burdock (*Arctium* spp.)) were attached to the loops of the fibres of his clothing. After several years of ridicule, de Mestral launched Velcro in 1955 as an alternative to zip-fasteners.[6]

Our desire to understand the world around us has also lead to a vast amount of folklore surrounding plants. Trees are a particularly rich source – unlike most plants they remain with us all year round and often outlive us. They provide some of the first signs of changing seasons and their leafless forms can appear other-worldly. Some believe we will suffer consequences if we offend plants – the removal of a hawthorn bush during the building of the DeLorean car factory in Northern Ireland in 1982 was blamed for the ill-fortune subsequently suffered by the business! And the company took this seriously enough to plant a replacement bush.[7] Even if you don't believe in the folklore, best not to take any chances!

The idea for this book came when I was asked where some of the flower remedies came from. I realised that I knew almost nothing about many of this very special group of plants. Getting to know these plants better has been immensely rewarding and enjoyable. But researching an existing set of plants can be a challenge – while many have been widely studied, some have only a very limited amount of information about them available. For this reason, I also looked at some close relations of the less-studied plants – as with humans, there are often a lot of features shared with close family members! And chemically, plants in the same genus and even the same family often share many compounds. I didn't attempt to list every chemical compound or every potential use of every plant, but rather I tried to find something interesting or unusual about each one.

The remedy plants are not arranged in alphabetical order. There is a logical ordering of the plants (logical to me, at least) based on links between them or their

Hawthorn (*Crataegus sp.*)

uses which I hope will be apparent as you make your way through the book. So now I hope you'll join me as we explore some of the molecules, remedies and lore of the plants of Dr Bach.

### References:

1. N. Weeks, (1973 edition); The Medical Discoveries of Edward Bach Physician, C.W. Daniel, ISBN 9780852070017, pp 48–9

2. E. Birben, U.M. Sahiner, C. Sackesen, S. Erzurum, O. Kalayci, (2012); Oxidative Stress and Antioxidant Defense; *World Allergy. Organ. J.*, 5(1), 9–19; doi: 10.1097/WOX.0b013e3182439613

3. C. Veeresham, (2012); *J. Adv. Pharm. Technol. Res.*, 3(4), 200–1, doi: 10.4103/2231-4040.104709

4. http://www.shinrin-yoku.org/shinrin-yoku.html [Accessed 15.10.17]

5. H. Ikei, M. Komatsu, C. Song, E. Himoro, Y. Miyazaki, (2014); The physiological and psychological relaxing effects of viewing rose flowers in office workers; *J. Physiol. Anthropol.*, 33:6; doi: 10.1186/1880-6805-33-6

6. T. Stephens, (4th January 2007); http://www.swissinfo.ch/eng/how-a-swiss-invention-hooked-the-world/5653568 [Accessed 11.10.17]

7. M. Freeman; http://www.druidry.org/library/trees/tree-lore-hawthorn [Accessed 11.10.17]

# Further Information:

## Making the Bach flower remedies from their source plants:

Two methods, the sun method and the boiling method, are used to prepare the so-called mother tinctures.

 In the sun method, flowers are placed on the surface of a thin glass bowl containing spring water for three or four hours, in direct sunlight. Twenty of the remedies are made using this method. In this book, these are indicated by the sun symbol alongside the remedy indications in the section title pages.

 The remaining eighteen remedies are made using the boiling method. This method is used for woodier plants and those which don't bloom when sunlight is strong. For these plants, the flowering part is boiled for half an hour in spring water. Remedies made by this method are indicated by the flask symbol shown, in the section title pages.

**Himalayan balsam (*Impatiens glandulifera*)**

The aim is the same for both methods – to transfer the energy or essence of the flowers to the water. This energised or potentised water is mixed with alcohol (in a 1:1 ratio) to produce the mother tincture. This is diluted again with alcohol to produce the stock bottles you can buy worldwide.

## Notes on chemical diagrams and references:

For some of the chemical compounds described a chemical diagram is included. This is a two-dimensional representation of the chemical structure, showing how atoms are joined together to form the compound. By convention, all unlabelled atoms are carbon (C) and these are assumed to have sufficient hydrogen atoms (H) attached to give standard valency (*i.e.* 4 single connections to other atoms). Non-carbon atoms, such as oxygen (O) and nitrogen (N) are shown with any attached H atoms.

References are included in each section. These are a mixture of web pages, news articles and scientific journal articles. In addition, the following books and websites were used extensively but are not referenced each time.

## Books:

E. Bach, (1941 edition); The Twelve Healers and Other Remedies, The Bach Centre, 2011; http://www.bachcentre.com/centre/download/healers.htm

M. Baker, (2013); Discovering the Folklore of Plants, 3rd edition, Shire Publications Ltd., ISBN 0747801789

R. Binney, (2016); Plant Lore and Legend, Rydon Publishing, ISBN 978-1-910821-10-7

T. Breverton, (2011); Breverton's Complete Herbal, Quercus Publishing Ltd., ISBN 978-0-85738-336-5

D. Hoffmann, (1996); Complete Illustrated Guide to the Holistic Herbal, Element Books, ISBN 0-00-713301-4

Mrs M. Grieve, (1973 edition); A Modern Herbal, Merchant Book Company Ltd., ISBN 1904779018

G. Kyd, M. Sibbons, (2014); Molecules, Medicines and Mischief A Year on the Chemical Trail around Cambridge University Botanic Garden, Vervain

Publishing, ISBN 978-0-9928998-0-6

B. Laws, (2010); Fifty Plants that Changed the Course of History, Quid Publishing, ISBN 978-0-85762-486-4

J.M. Paterson, (1996); Tree Wisdom, Thorsons, ISBN 978-0-7225-3408-3

D. Podlech, (2007 edition); Herbs and Healing Plants of Britain and Europe, HarperCollins, ISBN 978-0-26-167405-9

## Websites:

Bach Centre: http://www.bachcentre.com/

Chemspider: https://www.chemspider.com/

Pubmed: https://www.ncbi.nlm.nih.gov/pubmed

Royal Horticultural Society: https://www.rhs.org.uk/

Trees for Life: https://treesforlife.org.uk/

Woodland Trust: https://www.woodlandtrust.org.uk/

USDA Plants Database: https://plants.usda.gov/java/

**Disclaimer:** The text is solely intended for entertainment. Plants should not be used for medical purposes without seeking expert advice. The medicinal activities of plant material or chemical compounds are described for information only and this should not be taken to imply that they are or will be available for human use now or in the future.

For more information on herbal medicine it is recommended that one of the professional associations is consulted (*e.g.* European Herbal and Traditional Medicine Practitioners Association, http://ehtpa.eu/index.html or the National Institute of Medical Herbalists, https://www.nimh.org.uk/).

More information on Bach flower remedies can be obtained at www.cambridge-bach.co.uk and a list of registered practitioners and further information is available from the Bach Centre at www.bachcentre.com.

The Bach Centre garden

# Willow

## (*Salix vitellina*)

*Salix vitellina*, or golden willow, is usually considered to be a variety of white willow, *Salix alba* (making the name *Salix alba* var. *vitellina*). Golden willow is distinguished by its golden-yellow coloured stems. The tree is often coppiced or pollarded to utilise the colour of the young stems, particularly in winter gardens. The scarlet-stemmed variant *Salix alba* var. *vitellina* 'Britzensis' is used similarly. Coppicing involves cutting the trunk near ground level, while in pollarded trees the upper branches are removed. In both cases, numerous new shoots grow from the cut area. Both coppicing and pollarding are used in woodland management. In the case of willows, coppicing is carried out to produce branches or twigs for use in basket-making. Most willows produce flexible twigs (or osiers) which can bend without breaking. The exception is crack willow (*Salix fragilis*) which has twigs that break easily with a characteristic crack. Willows are fast-growing and the branches can be used for propagation. Driven into the earth to half-length in autumn, they will leaf in spring. If they are planted upside down the branches become roots and the roots become branches!

The medicinal use of willow bark was referenced by the ancient Egyptians in Ebers' medicinal papyrus (*ca.* 1500 BCE) and in Europe willow has been used since at least the time of Hippocrates (about 400 BCE). The introduction of compounds derived from the bark into modern-day medicine is attributed to the Rev. Edward Stone. He was suffering from agues (a collection of symptoms including intermittent

**Willow** is the Bach flower remedy for those who feel self-pity and resentment.

fever) and, walking in Oxfordshire, he decided to try chewing a piece of willow bark. He felt it helped his symptoms and, after testing the powdered bark on 50 of his friends, he reported its benefits in a letter to Lord Macclesfield at the Royal Society in 1763.[1]

His choice of willow bark was influenced by the abundance of the tree in the local area as he explained in his letter. This relates to the so-called Doctrine of Signatures, popularised by the Swiss physician Paracelsus.[2] The Doctrine stated that God had marked plants to show us how they could be used (so eyebright, *Euphrasia officinalis*, with flowers thought to resemble eyes, was used to treat eye conditions) or had placed them where they were needed. This may have led to scepticism about his report among the medical establishment, but the value of his discovery couldn't be denied.

The bark contains the compound salicin which is

Pollarded *Salix vitellina* 'Britzensis' in a winter garden

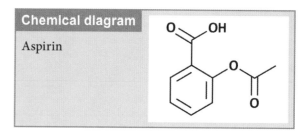

**Chemical diagram**

Aspirin

readily oxidised to give salicylates (ions of salicylic acid). In the tree, these have many roles including as allelopathic compounds, excreted into the soil to deter other plants from growing and competing with the willow for resources. In the human body, they act as COX enzyme inhibitors so reduce the production of prostaglandins which sensitise nerve endings to pain and cause inflammation.

However, the use of salicylates can cause the side-effect of stomach bleeding so, in 1890, the pharmaceutical company Bayer launched a project to look for a gentler alternative, one which retained the beneficial properties but with reduced (or ideally no) side-effects. Chemist Felix Hoffmann and his colleagues discovered that acetyl salicylic acid fitted the bill. Today this compound is better known as aspirin (the name is related to another source of salicin, meadowsweet, which was originally named by Carl Linnaeus as *Spiraea ulmaria*).[3]

Aspirin was the first of a new class of medicines known as non-steroidal anti-inflammatory drugs (NSAIDs) and became widely used for the treatment of pain and inflammation. It was the drug of choice used during the Spanish flu pandemic of 1918. Although the potential for causing stomach bleeding was reduced in aspirin, this remained a possible issue and increasingly use of the drug has been overtaken by newer drugs such as paracetamol and ibuprofen. However, the potential anti-coagulant side-effects have led to another use and many people now take a low daily dose of aspirin to help prevent heart attacks and strokes. It is also active against some types of cancer. Aspirin remains one of the most important and widely-used drugs on the market today, with an annual global usage of over 100 billion tablets.

Willow bark is still used by herbalists to treat pain, inflammation and fevers. Other chemicals present in the bark, such as flavonoids, may contribute to its success at relatively lower doses than aspirin. These may also reduce the occurrence of side-effects.

Willow has many other traditional medicinal uses.[4] The herbalist Culpeper recommended taking a drink made by mixing the boiled leaves or seeds in wine to extinguish the heat of lust in both men and women! Willow was also used to treat dyspepsia arising from weakness of the digestive organs. Other uses relied on the astringent properties of tannins in the bark to staunch bleeding and other humours[5] and to treat diarrhoea, worms and dysentery. It was considered to be a tonic and used in convalescence from acute diseases. Galen described using the burnt ashes of the bark, mixed with vinegar, to take away warts, corns and superfluous flesh. Today, salicylic acid (the parent salicylate) is used to treat warts, corns and verrucae. Traditionally, willow was believed to deter evil and bring good luck; the saying 'knock on wood' may have originated with the practice of knocking on a willow tree.

Willow is a popular material for biodegradable coffins. It has potential as a biofuel and is used in preference to oil for domestic and industrial heating in Sweden. Growth of willow for fuel can be combined with phytoremediation.[6] This is the decontamination of polluted water using trees. Run-off from landfill sites or industrial sites is applied to the willows. Organic pollutants and heavy metals are absorbed but the trees also benefit from the nutrients present in the water. Wood from *Salix alba* var. *caerulea* is used to make cricket bats as the tough, lightweight wood does not splinter easily. Trees are felled at 10 years old and each one produces around 32 cricket bats.

Since the 1960s, willow and poplar trees have been planted in the city of Beijing. Aimed at 'greening' the city, the tree-planting programme has had an unwanted side-effect. The fluff (or bast) shed in the spring can be a fire hazard and cause irritation to the respiratory system.[7] Over half of the fires in the city

*Salix alba*

**Female catkins with fluff**

during April 2017 were blamed on the catkin fluff by the municipal fire department.[8] The fluff is shed by female trees and carries the seeds in the wind after pollination. The seeds are therefore small and light, carry no food supply (endosperm) and have a short lifetime. Reducing the number of female trees would reduce the production of fluff and recently only male trees, which present less of a problem, have been planted.

Two possible methods to reduce the problems caused by existing female trees have been identified. Their upper branches can be removed and male branches grafted on but, although effective, this is time-consuming and expensive. During 2016, a chemical method was tested. A mixture of three plant chemicals which are growth promoters, including indole-3-butyric acid (IBA), was injected into 15,000 trees. These compounds inhibit flowering and promote vegetative growth and the injections are about 10 times less expensive than the alternative 'sex change surgery'.

IBA is an auxin, a plant hormone that promotes root formation, which occurs naturally in willows.

Both methods proved successful and will be combined with several other short- and long-term strategies as the local government attempts to solve the problems caused by the 2–3 million trees by 2020. Other methods include cutting down the trees, removing the shed

## Chemical diagram

Indole-3-butyric acid (IBA)

*Salix vitellina*

Golden weeping willow (*Salix* x *sepulcralis* 'Chrysocoma')

fluff manually and using a water jet to dampen down the fluff from the air or remove it from the trees.[9]

A tea made from willow stems was traditionally used by gardeners to encourage root growth.[10] Stems were placed in warm water for several days then removed. Cuttings dipped in the resultant 'willow water' before planting were found to root much faster. In fact, the water contained IBA which today is used in some commercial plant rooting products. The most common auxin is indole-3-acetic acid, similar to IBA but with two less carbon atoms.

Salicylates may have another role in trees. Researchers have found that walnut trees release methyl salicylate when under stresses like drought or unseasonal temperatures. This may trigger the formation of proteins that boost their defences and reduce energy use. However, it is also released into the atmosphere. Here it might 'warn' neighbouring plants of the threat and perhaps instigate an ecosystem-wide response.[11]

### References:

1. E. Stone, (1763); An account of the success of the bark of the willow in the cure of agues; *Phil. Trans.*, 53, 195–200; doi: 10.1098/rstl.1763.0033

2. http://www.sciencemuseum.org.uk/broughttolife/techniques/doctrine [Accessed 17.08.16]

3. http://www.aspirin-foundation.com/history-of-aspirin/100-years-of-aspirin/ [Accessed 18.08.16]

4. http://www.umm.edu/health/medical/altmed/herb/willow-bark [Accessed 18.08.16]

5. http://www.sciencemuseum.org.uk/broughttolife/techniques/humours [Accessed 23.08.16]

6. I. Dimitriou, P. Aronsson, (2005); Willows for energy and phytoremediation in Sweden; http://www.fao.org/docrep/008/a0026e/a0026e11.htm [Accessed 21.08.16]

7. http://www.rsc.org/chemistryworld/2016/05/hormone-injections-tackle-beijing-catkin-fluff-woes [Accessed 17.08.16]

8. Catkins cause fire hazards in Beijing; http://news.xinhuanet.com/english/2017-05/04/c_136256742.htm [Accessed 01.08.17]

9. M. Wu, C. Zhou, R. Li, (13th April 2017); Beijing Tree Pruners, Allergy Sufferers Stage Poplar Revolt; http://www.caixinglobal.com/2017-04-13/101078117.html [Accessed 01.08.2017]

10. http://guernsey.osu.edu/program-areas/master-gardener-volunteers/seasonal-gardening-tips/gardening-folklore [Accessed 17.08.16]

11. National Science Foundation, (18th September 2008); Walnut Trees Emit Aspirin-Like Chemical to Deal With Stress; News Release 08-159; https://www.nsf.gov/news/news_summ.jsp?cntn_id=112252 [Accessed 14.05.17]

# Aspen

## (*Populus tremula*)

Aspen bark is sometimes yellow-green due to the presence of chlorophyll, the magnesium-containing pigment which harvests the energy necessary for photosynthesis. Photosynthesis occurs in the inner bark and varies seasonally. It is most important during periods when there are no leaves. In fact, production of chlorophyll is proportionate to the light falling on the bark; when leaves are numerous, the bark is more shaded so chlorophyll production decreases. However, in winter when there are no leaves, chlorophyll accumulates in the bark and harvests the available sunlight. The resulting photosynthesis provides the tree with the fuel necessary to keep growing.[1] On the sunny side of open-growing aspen trees, the photo-synthetic bark produces a protective white powder which was used by First Nations peoples in Canada as a sunscreen.[2] As aspen is intolerant of the shade of other trees it is often found growing in isolation.

Leaf stalks (or petioles) are long, flattened and flexible near the leaf blade, allowing them to flutter and giving the tree its characteristic tremble or shiver. One traditional name for the tree was *langues de femmes* or women's tongues, likening the tremble to gossiping women who are never still. In fact, Satan was reputed to have given women speech by putting aspen leaves in their mouths![3] Placing an aspen leaf under the tongue was said to bestow eloquence. In Christian folklore, the tree was believed to shiver as its wood was used to make the Cross and it was the only tree which did not bow its head during the procession to Calvary. Alternatively, aspen was said to tremble

**Aspen** is the Bach flower remedy for those suffering from vague, unknown fears.

because it had the most acute hearing of any tree and moved continuously due to the news coming from afar. A crown made of aspen leaves was thought to provide its wearer with protection when visiting and returning from the Underworld and aspen crowns are sometimes found at ancient burial sites.

Aspen is a very efficient photosynthesiser and the trembling may prevent too much sunlight reaching the leaves where it could inhibit photosynthesis. Alternatively, it may maximise the supply of carbon dioxide and so allow photosynthesis to occur.[4] Aspen typically grows in damp conditions and the fluttering leaves may cause excess moisture to be evaporated. At the bottom of each leaf blade there are two small cups containing resin and these catch and absorb water, helping maintain water balance.

The bark and leaves contain salicylates (also found in birch and willow trees) and the related compound populin, the benzoate derivative of the salicylate precursor salicin. In salicin, the benzoate (PhCOO–) group on the left-hand side of the chemical diagram is replaced by –OH.[5] Salicin and benzoic acid can be produced from populin under alkaline conditions and salicin is also found in aspen bark.

**Chemical diagram**

Populin

The bark was traditionally used to treat intermittent fever (or agues), probably related to the presence of these compounds. Salicylates are still used medicinally today in the form of acetyl salicylic acid or aspirin (see willow section for more details). The idea that a shivering tree could be used to treat conditions where sufferers shiver is another example of the influence of the Doctrine of Signatures. A lock of hair (or some nail clippings) from the ague sufferer was sometimes attached to the tree with the idea that the tree would begin to shiver instead of the person!

Aspen wood pulp is used for books, newsprint and

fine printing papers. Other uses include in fibreboard, wafer board, sheathing, decking, boxes, crates, furniture parts, veneer, match sticks, tongue depressors, panelling and excelsior (a packing material consisting of fine wood shavings). The wood is also used to make oars, paddles and surgical splints and formerly was used in shields.

The Greek word *aspis*, meaning a round shield, gave the tree its name. As well as being the source of wood to make shields, there is also a traditional association of aspen with shielding from the darkness associated with fears. The tree was thought to offer protection of possessions; treasure was often buried under an aspen and a tree planted at the door of a house was believed to deter thieves.

Although aspen can reproduce sexually, it usually does so by growing shoots (suckers) from the root system. The aspen colonies this produces form a single organism of genetically identical clones which can be distinguished from nearby organisms by their identical behaviours. These single organisms can survive more than 1,000 years (although individual trees

**Adult leaves (left), juvenile (or sucker) leaf (right)**

within it survive for only up to about 150 years). Some American aspen (*Populus tremuloides*) colonies have been estimated to be among the largest single organisms. In 1997 Dr. Stewart Rood, of the University of Lethbridge, Alberta, is quoted[2] as estimating of the size of one clone near Salt Lake City, Utah, named 'Pando' as exceeding 5,000 tons, about three times greater than the largest giant sequoia tree. The Pando organism is believed to be over 80,000 years old and is 40 times heavier than a blue whale.[6]

**References:**

1. L.C. Pearson, D.B. Lawrence, (1958); Photosynthesis in Aspen Bark; *Am. J. Bot.*, 45(5), 383–7; http://www.jstor.org/stable/2439638

2. http://plantwatch.naturealberta.ca/choose-your-plants/aspen-poplar/ [Accessed 26.08.16]

3. T.F. Thiselton-Dyer, (1906); *Folk-Lore of Women*, Chapter V; http://www.sacred-texts.com/wmn/fow/fow07.htm [Accessed 27.08.16]

4. R. Griffith, (16th June 2015); Why are Aspen Leaves Always Trembling? Nature Insights; https://www.youtube.com/watch?v=QOdi-0IArBA [Accessed 24.08.16]

5. N.K. Richtmyer, E.H. Yeakel, (1934); The Structure of Populin; *J. Am. Chem. Soc.*, 56(11), 2495–7; doi: 10.1021/ja01326a090

6. http://www.fs.fed.us/wildflowers/beauty/aspen/grow.shtml [Accessed 27.08.16]

# Pine

*(Pinus sylvestris)*

The bark of Scots pine (*Pinus sylvestris*) is orange-brown and scaly, developing plates and fissures with age. The trees are sometimes called European redwoods and this term is used in the timber trade to indicate that imported wood is from Scandinavia or Russia. They are the only truly native pine trees in the UK and were abundant in the Caledonian Forest. Those found in the remnants of the Forest descend from the first pines which arrived in Scotland about 9,000 years ago. Today, the trees are widely planted to provide timber; Scots pine timber is one of the strongest softwoods and is used in the construction industry and joinery. It is also used to make telegraph poles, gate posts and fencing. Groups of conifers, particularly pines, often occur in groups of seven known as Seven Sisters. Legend has it only six will flourish and the seventh will die, no matter how often it is replaced.

Leaves, or needles, occur in pairs, joined at the base by a sheath. A coat of wax over the green needles gives them a grey-blue hue. Needles are shed every 3 years, with pairs still joined together. Male and female flowers are produced on the same tree. Male flowers release bright yellow pollen in large quantities, sometimes nicknamed 'sulfur showers'. Small, female flowers occur at the tip of the spring shoots and consist of scales which point upward. They produce mucilage which can catch and draw pollen down towards the ovules. Once fertilisation occurs, the scales thicken and join up. After at least a year, these cones open to release the seeds. The cones close when it rains and open again when it's dry because

**Pine** is the Bach flower remedy for those suffering feelings of guilt.

the seeds are wind-borne and would drop to the base of the tree in wet conditions. In the autumn, empty cones drop off. At any one time, branches can contain three generations of cones *i.e.* new, fertilised and sealed, and empty.

The tree can be tapped for a resin which is distilled to make turpentine. This was used in traditional medicine to treat wounds and internally to treat parasites. It was considered to have antiseptic and diuretic properties and was taken using an inhaler or as a chest rub to relieve cold symptoms and other throat and nasal conditions. A pillow stuffed with pine needles was believed to soothe chest complaints. Today, the well-known chest rub Vick's VapoRub still contains oil of turpentine. However, the major uses of turpentine are as a solvent, for example, to thin paints,

and as a source of starting materials for the chemical industry. This latter use is primarily due to the major components of the turpentine, α- and β-pinene.

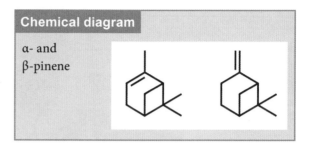

| Chemical diagram |
| --- |
| α- and β-pinene |

These volatile monoterpenes are closely related, having the same formula and differing only in the position of the double bond. They are also found in oils of rosemary, orange peel and eucalyptus. When given off by the tree, they interact with other compounds in the atmosphere such as ozone to produce nanoparticles. The particles are Rayleigh scatterers and split white light from the sun into its component colours. As blue light is scattered most, the trees are surrounded by a blue haze; the Blue Ridge Mountains of Virginia and the Blue Mountains in Australia get their names from this effect as they are covered with pine or eucalyptus trees, respectively. The production of this haze gives the trees some degree of temperature control.

The inner bark of pine trees was traditionally used to make rope and a dye was prepared from the cones. Pine tar can be made by burning the tree (traditionally the roots and stumps) in a closed container; charcoal is also produced. Although the stumps give the highest quality tar, these are in relatively short supply and today pine wood is more commonly used. In Scandinavia, pine tar was produced by a single Swedish company who termed their product Stockholm tar and this was a common wood preservative.[1] Tar was also used on ships to waterproof ropes and sailors' hands would become stained. As a result, British Navy seamen became known as Jack Tars or simply tars. Medicinally, pine tar is used in the form of a soap to treat skin conditions including psoriasis and eczema. In veterinary medicine, it is applied to the hooves of cattle and horses to condition and

hydrate them and as an antiseptic to treat infections.

Pine essential oil is used in aromatherapy to reduce inflammation, protect against sinus infections, clear mucus and phlegm, cure skin conditions like eczema and psoriasis, boost the immune system, fight fungal and viral infections, stimulate the mind and body and protect the home and body from a wide variety of germs. The smell of pine is associated with cleanliness and its fragrance is often added to home-cleaning products.

The extract from the heartwood of Scots pine forms the basis of a range of products for human or animal use.[2] These include toothpaste and mouthwash, shower gel and soaps and even a shampoo for camels![3] These uses rely on the antibacterial and germicidal properties of compounds found in the wood. A range of items made of so-called hygienic pine wood is also available and includes germ-resistant pens, bath mats claimed to prevent athlete's foot and bed boards that reduce the occurrence of dust mites. Plants can also

be treated with a mixture of the pine extract and water for prevention of disease and insect infestation.[2]

Beers made with spruce or pine needles or shoots were introduced to Britain by the Vikings. They contain vitamin C and were sometimes drunk by sailors to prevent scurvy, including by Captain Cook and his crew.[4] Shetland spruce ale was reputed to stimulate animal instincts and give you twins![4] Alba, a beer brewed to a traditional Highland recipe from Scots pine and spruce shoots, is still available today. Pure malted barley is boiled with young sprigs of pine for several hours before fresh shoots of spruce are added for a short infusion before fermentation.[4]

A tea made with the needles and bark of coniferous trees, possibly pine, was drunk to cure scurvy by the French explorer Jacques Cartier and his men in the 16th century, at the behest of the natives of the St. Lawrence region of Canada.[5] The trees were named Annedda by the local people and Cartier's reports of the success of using these 'trees of life' led to interest in Europe. Later, it was found that, apart from vitamin C, the bark also contains bioflavonoids with strong antioxidant activity and amino acids which may work in synergy to bring about the observed cure.[5]

Professor Jack Masquelier first identified oligomeric proanthocyanidins (OPCs) in peanut shells and went on to develop and patent a technique to extract them from pine bark. In other work, he identified OPCs as a co-factor of vitamin C (important in Cartier's scurvy cure), extracted OPCs from grape seeds and identified a range of beneficial medicinal effects.[6]

OPCs are biopolymers made up of procyanidins such as catechin and its stereoisomer epicatechin.

Catechins occur in many plants and epicatechin is believed to be the source of the health benefits of dark chocolate, including the promotion of muscle-building![7]

The extract obtained from maritime pine (*Pinus pinaster* or *Pinus maritima*) is sometimes known as Pycnogenol. There are numerous health benefits attributed to Pycnogenol including for the treatment of type 2 diabetes and reduction of diabetic retinopathy, reduction of LDL cholesterol, improvement in physical performance and endurance in athletes and reduction of high blood pressure. A large and ever-increasing number of studies and promising reviews

## Chemical diagram

Epicatechin

*Pinus* sp.

of its activity have been published.[8,9,10] However, in 2012, a Cochrane review concluded that there was insufficient evidence to support its use to treat any chronic disorder. This conclusion was based on the small size of the studies completed so far and the risk of bias.[11]

## References:

1. T.P. Kaye, (1997); Pine Tar; History and Uses; San Francisco Maritime National Park Association; http://www.maritime.org/conf/conf-kaye-tar.htm [Accessed 07.09.16]

2. http://www.wilms.com/Hygiene/En/Default.aspx [Accessed 07.09.16]

3. K. Watson, (3rd June 2012); 'I developed camel shampoo'; BBC World News; http://www.bbc.co.uk/news/ business-18294887 [Accessed 07.09.16]

4. http://www.grogandgruel.co.uk/drink/the-beer/ williams-brothers-brewing/ [Accessed 06.09.16]

5. D.J. Durzan, (2009); Arginine, scurvy and Cartier's "tree of life."; *J. Ethnobiol. Ethnomed.*, 5:5; doi: 10.1186/1746-4269-5-5

6. J. Spounias, (21st June 2015); The Mysterious 'Vitamin P'; *American Free Press*; http://americanfreepress.net/ the-mysterious-vitamin-p/ [Accessed 04.08.17]

7. PricePlow Blog, (8th January 2015, Updated to August 2016); Epicatechin: The Dark Force Behind Dark Chocolate; https://blog.priceplow.com/epicatechin

8. P. Rohdewald, (2002); A review of the French maritime pine bark extract (Pycnogenol), a herbal medication with a diverse clinical pharmacology; *Int. J. Clin. Pharmacol. Ther.*, 40(4),158–68; doi: 10.5414/CPP40158

9. Scientific and Clinical Monologue for Proprietary Botanical Ingredient Pycnogenol (French Maritime Pine Bark Extract) *Pinus pinaster* Aiton subsp. *atlantica* [Fam. Pinaceae]; American Botanical Council; http://abc.herbalgram.org/site/DocServer/ Pycnog_FullMono120809_LOW.pdf?docID=1741

10. Horphag Research; http://www.pycnogenol.com/science/ bibliography/ [Accessed 04.08.17]

11. A. Schoonees, J. Visser, A. Musekiwa, J. Volmink, (2012); Pycnogenol® (extract of French maritime pine bark) for the treatment of chronic disorders; *Cochrane Database Syst.* Rev., Issue 4, Art. No.: CD008294; doi: 10.1002/14651858.CD008294.pub4

# The Horse Chestnuts

## (*Aesculus* spp.)

Two remedies are made from the horse chestnut (*Aesculus hippocastanum*) – **Chestnut Bud** (from the buds) and **White Chestnut** (from the blossom) – and one from red horse chestnut (or **Red Chestnut**, *Aesculus* x *carnea*).

 **Chestnut Bud** is the Bach flower remedy for those who do not learn from past mistakes.

 **White Chestnut** is the Bach flower remedy for those suffering from unwanted, repetitive thoughts.

 **Red Chestnut** is the Bach flower remedy for those whose over-caring for loved ones results in constant worrying.

Horse chestnuts are native to the Balkans and were introduced into the UK in the 16th century. Their showy clusters of flowers, resembling candelabra, made them a popular planting in formal gardens and public parks. The flower petals have a yellow blotch which turns red once the flower has been pollinated. This directs bees to the flowers which still require pollination; the red colour will appear black to the bees, making the flower unattractive. Unopened buds are tightly stuck together with a resin which protects the leaves and flowers inside from damp and frost. When the sun melts the resin, the shoots develop quickly, within three to four weeks.

The shiny nuts from the horse chestnut tree, also known as conkers, were collected during World War I to provide a source of starch. Schoolchildren, scouts and members of women's groups including the WI (Women's Institute) were paid to collect them, although they were not told why the nuts were needed. In fact, they were taken to factories in Holton Heath and King's Lynn where they were used to make the solvent acetone, using the so-called Weizmann process.[1]

Acetone was needed for the manufacture of cordite for the munitions industry. Initially, maize was used

**Horse chestnut**

as a source of starch and alternatives included other grains and potatoes. However, by 1917 imports of maize from USA were in doubt due to the presence of German U-boats in the Atlantic. Alternative sources of starch were considered too important for food use. However, although starch could be obtained from conkers, they were not a very effective source partly due to their thick skin. Despite this, their use did contribute to maintaining the supply of acetone during the latter stages of the war.[2]

Weizmann's bacterial fermentation process ultimately produced 20,000[2] tonnes of acetone in the UK and was also utilised in the USA and Canada. Chaim Weizmann was a leading Zionist as well as a chemist and his contribution to the war effort is partially credited for Britain's support for the setting up the state of Israel. In 1949 Weizmann became its first president.

Although conkers are unfit for use as human food, they can be used as feed for livestock. During World War I it was estimated that for every ton harvested and fed to livestock, half a ton of grain for human consumption could be saved. However, conkers are slightly toxic to some animals including horses.

In spite of this, ground up conkers were traditionally used to treat chest conditions in horses.

This use is one possible origin for the name horse chestnut, although perhaps the name suggested the use, rather than the other way around. Other possibilities include that 'horse' is a corruption of the Welsh *gwres*, meaning fierce, hot or pungent, contrasting the nuts with those of the sweet chestnut tree (*Castanea sativa*) which are edible. A final suggestion is that it

**Conkers**

relates to the markings left on twigs by the leaf blades. These resemble inverted horseshoes, complete with nail holes and the twigs can also look like horses' feet and fetlocks. In the USA, conkers are sometimes known as buckeyes due to their resemblance to deer's (buck's) eyes.

Extracts of horse chestnut seeds are used in herbal medicine to treat conditions of the veins such as varicose veins and haemorrhoids. They contain a group of chemical compounds known collectively as aescin which includes β-aescin, medicinally the most important. The extract has undergone clinical trials and a Cochrane Review concluded it was both safe and useful for the short-term treatment of chronic venous insufficiency (poor blood flow through the veins, usually in the legs). One trial indicated that this treatment was as good as wearing compression stockings, the commonly used treatment.[3]

As well as oral use of the extract, it is sometimes used in a gel for the legs and is an ingredient of Badedas bath products. Aescin has potential use as an anti-ageing component in skincare products.[4] This is because it has antioxidant properties, reduces the fragility of capillaries (reducing fluid leakage) and generates contraction forces in fibroblasts.[5] Fibroblasts are a type of cell involved in making connective tissue. The generation of fibroblast contraction forces is linked with a reduction in the appearance of wrinkles. Extracts can also reduce the number and size of membrane pores so reducing fluid leakage into the

**Horse chestnut leaves**

surrounding tissue.[6] Other beneficial uses include as an anti-inflammatory agent, to prevent oedema and to treat inner-ear conditions.[6]

Saponins like aescin are insect-repellent.[7] This could be behind the old wives' tale that conkers placed around windows and doors deter spiders from coming inside. In 2009, the Royal Society of Chemistry ran a competition for schoolchildren to design an experiment to test the theory but the winning entry appeared to disprove it.[8] Similarly, scientists at the John Innes Centre in Norwich looked at the issue in 2014[9] and found no evidence to support conkers' spider-deterring reputation. However, some commercial anti-spider sprays contain extract of horse chestnut seeds and product reviews suggest they may be effective.

## Chemical diagram

### β-Aescin

## Chemical diagram

### Aesculin

Horse chestnut flowers

Twig showing leaf scars and buds

Red horse chestnut

Bark extracts were traditionally used as a tonic and for their fever-reducing and narcotic properties. The bark and leaves contain the compound aesculin. This is an antioxidant and protects against DNA damage and UV-B radiation. It also has vasoprotective and anti-inflammatory effects and has been used in some skincare products.[10] Aesculin is the glycoside of aesculetin (*i.e.* addition of a glucose group to aesculetin gives aesculin) and the conversion of aesculin to aesculetin is the basis of a test for certain types of bacteria. Only some bacteria convert aesculin to aesculetin and glucose, in the presence of bile. The formation of aesculetin is shown chemically by reaction with ferric citrate in agar to produce dark-coloured phenolic compounds.[11] Taken orally, aesculin causes gastroenteritis and in large quantities can result in lack of coordination, paralysis or muscle weakness.[12]

Horse chestnut trees often suffer attack by leaf-miner moth (*Cameraria ohridella*) larvae. The damage occurs after flowering, with the leaves turning partially white then brown. This may weaken the tree by reducing its ability to photosynthesise, leading to an early fall of leaves. Although the effects are unsightly, the tree is not killed by the infestation but it may be more susceptible to other infections. Over the winter, pupae can be found in the tree's leaf litter so removal of this and careful composting can prevent the moths emerging in spring.[13]

A bleeding canker which now affects over 50% of the UK's horse chestnut trees is more deadly and can kill the trees.[14] Bleeding cankers (bark infections) have long been known in horse chestnut trees and can be caused by bacteria or fungi. The current rapid increase in occurrence is believed to be due to a bacterium, *Pseudomonas syringae* pv. *aesculi*. Currently there is no widespread treatment for this canker and trees are commonly removed and burned to prevent infection spreading further. A possible treatment may lie in the use of the potent antibacterial compound allicin, obtained from garlic.[15] This is produced by garlic as part of its defence mechanism, but is unstable. However, stabilised allicin can now be obtained and injection of this into an infected tree can successfully treat the infection. In fact, treatment with allicin is found to be more than 95% effective. And what's more, the treatment also reduces attack by leaf-miner moths.[16] This might be the result of a side-effect of allicin injection — the trees smell like garlic!

Red horse chestnut (*Aesculus* x *carnea*) is a hybrid of horse chestnut and red buckeye (*Aesculus pavia*). The trees are generally smaller than horse chestnuts with deep pink flowers. The flowers also have yellow blotches, turning red after pollination like white horse chestnut flowers do. The trees can be affected by bleeding canker[14] but are only attacked by leaf-miner moths if they grow near heavily infested horse chestnut trees.[17]

**Red horse chestnut flowers**

**References:**

1. S. David, (2nd February 2012); Did conkers help win the First World War?; History Extra; http://www.historyextra.com/conker [Accessed 30.08.16]

2. Holton Heath, Solent: Conkers to Cordite (12th February 2014); http://www.bbc.co.uk/programmes/p01s4xcw [Accessed 30.08.16]

3. M.H. Pittler, E. Ernst, (2012); Horse chestnut seed extract for chronic venous insufficiency; *Cochrane Database Syst. Rev.*; Issue 11, Art. No.: CD003230; doi: 10.1002/14651858. CD003230.pub4

4. J.A. Wilkinson, A.M.G. Brown, (1999); Horse Chestnut – *Aesculus Hippocastanum*: Potential Applications in Cosmetic Skin-care Products; *Int. J. Cosmetic Sci.*, 21(6); 437–47; doi: 10.1046/j.1467-2494.1999.234192.x

5. T. Fujimura, K. Tsukahara, S. Moriwaki, M. Hotta, T. Kitahara, Y. Takema, (2006); A horse chestnut extract, which induces contraction forces in fibroblasts, is a potent anti-aging ingredient; *J. Cosmetic Sci.*, 57(5), 369–376; http://journal.scconline.org/abstracts/cc2006/cc057n05/p00369-p00376.html

6. Monograph, (2009); *Altern. Med. Rev.*, 14(3), 278–83; http://www.altmedrev.com/archives

7. I. Chaieb, (2010); Saponins as insecticides: a review; *Tunisian Journal of Plant Protection*, 5(1), 39–50; http://www.iresa.agrinet.tn/tjpp/SiteWeb/PreviousIssues/TJPP5-1/4Ikbal.pdf

8. Royal Society of Chemistry, (15th July 2010); Pupils scoop prize for unravelling conker theory; http://www.rsc.org/AboutUs/News/PressReleases/2010/Conkerswin.asp [Accessed 30.08.16]

9. Professor Ian Bedford, (2016); John Innes Centre, Norwich; Personal communication

10. M. Saini, A.A. Khan, M. Bala, M.Z. Abdin, H. Farooqi, (2014); Development of a validated HPTLC method for quantification of esculin in different fractions of *Cichorium intybus* leaf extract; *Int. J. Pharm. Pharm. Sci.*, 6(1), 478–82 (incorrectly printed as 278–82 in print version); http://www.ijppsjournal.com/Vol6Issue1/8203.pdf

11. UK Standards for Microbiology Investigations TP 2: Aesculin hydrolysis test; TP 2i3 November 2014; https://www.gov.uk/government/publications/smi-tp-2-aesculin-hydrolysis-test [Accessed 30.08.16]

12. http://www.rightdiagnosis.com/p/plant_poisoning_aesculin/ [Accessed 30.08.16]

13. Forestry Commission; Horse chestnut leaf miner – (*Cameraria ohridella*); http://www.forestry.gov.uk/horsechestnutleafminer [Accessed 30.08.16]

14. Royal Horticultural Society; Horse chestnut bleeding canker; https://www.rhs.org.uk/advice/profile?PID=183 [Accessed 30.08.16]

15. C. Marshall, (7th October 2014); Garlic injection could tackle tree diseases; http://www.bbc.co.uk/news/science-environment-29522647 [Accessed 31.08.16]

16. https://www.jcaac.com/hope-for-britains-horse-chestnut-trees/ [Accessed 30.08.16]

17. Forest Research; Impact of horse-chestnut leaf miner *Cameraria ohridella* on horse-chestnut trees; https://www.forestry.gov.uk/fr/beeh-9r2n94 [Accessed 05.08.17]

# Sweet Chestnut

## (*Castanea sativa*)

Native to Southern Europe, the sweet chestnut was introduced to Britain by the Romans, who ground the nuts to make a flour or coarse meal they used to make porridge. The nuts are smaller and more edible than conkers and are covered in spiny, protective husks called cupules which protect them from squirrels and other predators. Cupules usually contain two to four nuts. John Evelyn, the English gardener and diarist, wrote that chestnuts were 'delicacies for princes and a lusty and masculine food for rustics, and able to make women well-complexioned'. However, although commonly eaten in other parts of Europe, in England chestnuts were usually fed to the pigs.

The best chestnuts reputedly come from marrons, *i.e.* varieties that produce one or sometimes two larger seeds per fruit or cupule, with an easily-removable inner skin. These chestnuts contain about 15% sugar. The nuts can be eaten raw, roasted or candied to form marrons glacés. Roasted chestnuts are traditionally used as a stuffing for turkey. A meal made from chestnuts was sometimes used to whiten linen cloth or for making starch.

Cooking food changes its chemical composition, nutritional value, colour and flavour. When chestnuts are roasted, the volatile compounds γ-butyrolactone and furfural are formed.[1] The former has a sweet, caramel flavour and the latter a woody, almond flavour. But the compounds produced are not always beneficial; acrylamide, a probable human carcinogen

**Sweet Chestnut** is the Bach flower remedy for those suffering from anguish and deep despair.

**Marrons glacés**

and known neurotoxin, is also produced.[1] The median acrylamide content of commercial samples of roasted chestnuts was found to be 90 μg/kg. In 2009, tolerable daily limits were estimated; 2.6 μg/kg body weight/day based on the carcinogenic effects and 40 μg/kg body weight/day based on the neurotoxicity. For a 70 kg person, in the absence of any other sources, this would suggest that eating up to 2 kg of roasted chestnuts per day would be safe![2,3] However, avoiding acrylamide is difficult as it is found in any starchy food heated above 120°C, including biscuits, crisps, toast *etc.* Currently there are no regulatory limits to the quantity of acrylamide present in food, but the public and food manufacturers have been encouraged to take steps to reduce acrylamide formation and intake.[4]

| Chemical diagram | |
| --- | --- |
| Acrylamide | 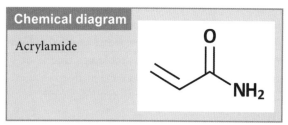 |

γ-Butyrolactone or GBL occurs in small quantities in some wines but for commercial use it is synthesised. As well as its use as a flavouring, it is a solvent and reagent in the chemical industry. It can dissolve cured superglue. Although not medicinally active, GBL is a prodrug for γ-hydroxybutyric acid or GHB. This

means that it is metabolised in the body to produce GHB, a compound which produces intoxication like that of alcohol.[5]

GHB is used recreationally, to increase athletic performance and sometimes as a date-rape drug. Medicinally, it can be used to treat narcolepsy and was formerly used in anaesthesia. In the UK, GBL and GHB are class C drugs so possession or sale for human consumption is illegal. GBL is permitted for use as a food flavouring or other legitimate uses, but this must be registered.[6]

| Chemical diagram | |
| --- | --- |
| γ-Butyrolactone (GBL) | 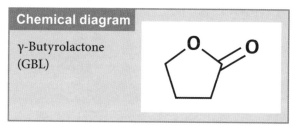 |

Furfural is produced commercially from agricultural by-products like oat hulls. The name comes from *furfur*, Latin for bran. The Quaker Oats Company was first to commercially exploit oat hulls to produce furfural, at its cereal mill at Cedar Rapids, Iowa. Furfural is used as a chemical feedstock and solvent, notably in the refining of lubricating oils.[7] It can also be produced from wood chips and this may allow any increase in demand to be met. It has a potential use in the production of furans, including tetrahydrofuran (THF), if increasing oil prices render the alternative routes to THF from petroleum too expensive.[8] Although it is used as a flavouring agent in low concentrations and is naturally present in some foods, furfural is toxic at high concentrations[9] and can act as a skin irritant.[10]

The Romans valued chestnut flower honey for its taste. Today it is used for dressing wounds, skin ulcers and burns due to its antibacterial and antioxidant properties.[1] Leaves were chewed or made into a tea to treat fevers. The major medicinal use, however, was to treat paroxysmal and convulsive coughs such as whooping-cough and other conditions of the respiratory system.

Leaf extracts contain a variety of compounds derived from ursene and oleanene. The extracts have been shown to disarm *Staphylococcus aureus* bacteria by shutting off their ability to produce toxins. This could provide a new method of preventing and treating MRSA infections.[11] Extracts do not kill the bacteria, but disrupt bacterial communication or quorum sensing. Importantly, they do not harm the skin cells or the normal skin micro-flora and do not appear to create resistance. Work on identifying the compounds responsible for this action is ongoing, but the new mechanism represents an important step forward in the treatment of drug-resistant bacterial infections.[12]

Chestnut wood is more durable than oak although it loses durability after 50 years old. It is used when wood must be sunk into the ground. In South East England, sweet chestnut is coppiced to produce poles.

A 250-year-old sweet chestnut tree was the focus of an anti-road protest in London in 1993. The tree, on George Green in Wanstead, was to be cut down to make way for an extension to the M11 motorway. Protestors slept in it for five weeks before they were evicted. Removal of the tree was also challenged in court. One argument was that, as letters were delivered there by the Royal Mail, it constituted a legal dwelling. The tree was eventually cut down in December 1993.[13]

**References:**

1. M.C.B.M. De Vasconcelos, R.N. Bennett, E.A.S. Rosa, J.V. Ferreira-Cardoso, (2010); Composition of European chestnut (*Castanea sativa* Mill.) and association with health effects: fresh and processed products; *J. Sci. Food Agric.*, 90(10), 1578–89; doi: 10.1002/jsfa.4016

2. L. Karasek, T. Wenzl, E. Anklam, (2009); Determination of acrylamide in roasted chestnuts and chestnut-based foods by isotope dilution HPLC-MS/MS; *Food Chem.*, 114(4), 1555–8; doi: 10.1016/j.foodchem.2008.11.057

3. R.G. Tardiff, M.L. Gargas, C.R. Kirman, M.L. Carson, L.M. Sweeney, (2010); Estimation of safe dietary intake levels of acrylamide for humans; *Food Chem. Toxicol.*, 48(2), 658–67; doi: 10.1016/j.fct.2009.11.048

4. https://www.food.gov.uk/science/acrylamide-0 [Accessed 05.08.17]

5. NIH U.S. National Library of Medicine; TOXNET; Hazardous Substances Database: Butyrolactone; https://toxnet.nlm.nih.gov/cgi-bin/sis/search2/r?dbs+hsdb:@term+@rn+96-48-0 [Accessed 01.09.16]

6. http://www.drugwise.org.uk/ghb/ [Accessed 31.08.16]

7. International Furan Chemicals; http://www.furan.com/

furfural.html [Accessed 05.08.17]

8. J. Ebert; Biomass Magazine; http://biomassmagazine. com/articles/1950/furfural-future-feedstock-for-fuels- and-chemicals [Accessed 01.09.16]

9. International Programme on Chemical Safety, World Health Organisation, Safety Evaluation of Certain Food Additives, WHO Food Additives Series: 42, 1999; http://www.inchem.org/documents/jecfa/jecmono/ v042je03.htm [Accessed 01.09.16]

10. The National Institute for Occupational Safety and Health (NIOSH); NIOSH Pocket Guide to Chemical Hazards; Furfural, (updated 11th April 2016); http://www.cdc.gov/ niosh/npg/npgd0297.html [Accessed 01.09.16]

11. Science Daily, (21st August 2015); Chestnut leaves yield extract that disarms deadly staph bacteria; https://www.sciencedaily.com/releases/2015/08/ 150821164150.htm [Accessed 31.08.16]

12. C.L. Quave, J.T. Lyles, J.S. Kavanaugh, K. Nelson, C.P. Parlet, H.A. Crosby, K.P. Heilmann, A.R. Horswill, (2015); *Castanea sativa* (European Chestnut) Leaf Extracts Rich in Ursene and Oleanene Derivatives Block *Staphylococcus aureus* Virulence and Pathogenesis without Detectable Resistance; *PLoS ONE*, 10(8), e0136486; doi: 10.1371/ journal.pone.0136486

13. http://news.bbc.co.uk/onthisday/hi/dates/stories/ december/7/newsid_2536000/2536089.stm [Accessed 31.08.16]

**Cupules**

# Walnut

## (*Juglans regia*)

Native to regions east of the Balkans including Iran, the common or Persian walnut is now widespread in Britain where it is sometimes known as the English walnut. The tree was called *nux Gallica* by the Romans who may have introduced it to the UK. They associated it with love and marriage and at weddings the nuts were thrown to bring fertility. The English name walnut may have derived from the Germanic names *Wallnuss* or *Welsche Nuss* (foreign nut).

The tree was believed to fruit better if the nuts were beaten off and this is alluded to in the couplet,

> 'A woman, a dog and a walnut tree,
> The more you beat them, the better they be'.

However, UK temperatures are not conducive to nut formation. This may have led to the English tradition of pickling walnuts. The process begins with picking the whole fruit, or drupe, before the shell and kernel have formed inside. These are soaked in brine (salt and water) then dried. They are now bottled in a pickling vinegar containing spices or, more usually, boiled in a pickling syrup containing vinegar, sugar and spices. Pickled walnuts are traditionally eaten with cheese and associated with the Christmas season.[1]

The nuts contain a significant amount of α-linolenic acid, an omega-3 fatty acid. This can reduce the chances of developing heart disease and is active against breast cancer. Walnuts can reduce inflammation and joint pain in rheumatoid arthritis and inhibit the growth and reduce the size of prostate tumours. Walnuts were rated the number one nut

> **Walnut** is the Bach flower remedy for those who need protection from outside influences or the effects of change.

in a study comparing the antioxidant properties of 9 types.[2] An added benefit is that they are usually eaten raw whereas other nuts are often roasted, reducing the quality of the antioxidants. These antioxidants were estimated to be between 2 and 15 times more potent than vitamin E. What's more, eating only 7 walnuts a day will provide all the health benefits of walnuts discovered so far.[2]

Traditionally, the bark and leaves were used to treat skin conditions such as herpes, eczema, ulcers and scrofulous diseases (*i.e.* diseases resembling or due to tuberculosis of the lymph glands). The husks and leaves were used as a treatment for worms and the juice of the green husks was gargled with honey to treat sore mouths or throats. The skin coating the kernel was dried and powdered and used to treat colic. The seed oil was also used to treat colic and, externally, to treat skin conditions and wounds. The oil was sometimes known as vegetable arsenic as the skin conditions it was used for were otherwise treated with arsenic.

Followers of the Doctrine of Signatures, believing God marked plants to tell us how they could be used, advocated use of the kernels to treat conditions of the brain and the outer husks for wounds to the head. Husks or kernels were sometimes burned and used with oil and wine to stop hair falling out and to lighten the colour. A piece of green husk was placed in a hollow tooth to relieve pain.

Limited trials of the leaf extract have shown beneficial effects in the treatment of type 2 diabetes. The extract caused a reduction in cholesterol, triglyceride and HbA1c (haemoglobin bound glucose) levels, with no adverse effects.[3] The leaves were used in Austrian folk medicine to treat diabetes and have been demonstrated to act as a PTP1B enzyme inhibitor. This enzyme is linked to insulin sensitivity and obesity as well as to breast cancer.[4] Other proven effects of the leaf extract include as an antioxidant and antitumour agent.[5]

Walnut wood was used for making Queen Anne furniture. This was popular in the period from just before to just after the reign of the British monarch

(1702–1714). The period was known as 'the age of walnut' as walnut wood replaced oak as the wood of choice among furniture-makers of the time. The distinctive features of the style were the presence of cabriole legs (double curved) and curved backs to the chairs which fitted the curve in the hollow of the spine.[6] The source of the trees for English furniture-makers was the French Savoie region, but in 1709 a severe winter damaged about two thirds of the region's trees. Export of the wood was banned in 1720 and mahogany began to be used instead. Walnut wood is still used today in veneers and inlays and has a value four times that of oak.[7]

Walnut oil is sometimes used in salad dressings or for cooking. It is also used as a medium for pigments in oil paints. It is a drying oil *i.e.* it undergoes chemical changes when exposed to oxygen which cause it to harden.[8] The oil yellows less than linseed oil, a popular alternative, but does tend to become rancid quickly. Renaissance painter Leonardo da Vinci sometimes used walnut oil paints. He wrote about the detrimental effect of the husks on the quality of the paint, saying the colouring matter of the husk would rise to the surface of the painting and cause it to change.[8]

The compound juglone, or nucin, occurs in the bark, husks and elsewhere in the tree, but not in the kernels. It is stored in a non-toxic form (as the glucoside) but juglone is released on exposure to oxygen. It is an allelopathic compound, leached into the surrounding soil to deter other plants from growing; originally this effect of walnut trees was known as 'walnut wilt'.[9] Juglone is also toxic to some insects, fish and micro-organisms including bacteria and fungi. It is active against *Helicobacter pylori*, a bacterium affecting around 50% of the world's population. It has antitumour activity and its antifungal properties make it useful in the treatment of athlete's foot and ringworm. Current medicinal use is limited to its sedative effect on animals. Other potential uses are as a herbicide and biocide.[9] The effect of walnuts on insects meant that walnut leaves were traditionally strewn around a stable or house. Coachmen sometimes sponged

Side chair, c. 1740, firm of Giles Grendey, England, bur walnut and walnut veneers, Art Institute of Chicago

horses with a solution of the steeped leaves. Cattle were noted to gather in the shade of walnut trees, perhaps benefiting from the lack of insects there.

Juglone is related to lawsone (from henna) and plumbagin (found in *Ceratostigma willmottianum* (cerato) and other leadworts). It is an orange-brown colouring agent used in the food and cosmetics industries and can also be used in inks and dyes.[9,10] Walnut husks form a brown dye, used to colour hair or fabrics. The dye doesn't require a fixative so the husks will stain the hands if handled without gloves. Husks can also cause skin irritation. When nuts are sold in their shells, these have often been washed to remove any traces of the dyeing compounds.

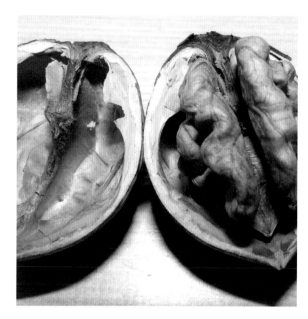

**Chemical diagram**

Juglone

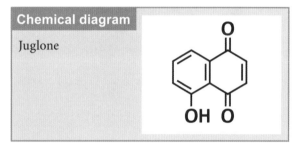

### References:

1. http://www.graftedwalnuts.co.uk/health.html#pickling [Accessed 04.09.16]

2. American Chemical Society, (27th March 2011); Walnuts are top nut for heart-healthy antioxidants; http://www.acs.org/content/acs/en/pressroom/newsreleases/2011/march/walnuts-are-top-nut-for-heart-healthy-antioxidants.html [Accessed 04.09.16]

3. S. Hosseini, L. Jamshidi, S. Mehrzadi, K. Mohammad, A.R. Najmizadeh, H. Alimoradi, H.F. Huseini, (2014); Effects of *Juglans regia* L. leaf extract on hyperglycemia and lipid profiles in type two diabetic patients: A randomized double-blind, placebo-controlled clinical trial; *J. Ethnopharmacol.*, 152(3), 451–6; doi: 10.1016/j.jep.2014.01.012

4. A. Pitschmann, M. Zehl, A.G. Atanasov, V.M. Dirsch, E. Heiss, S. Glasl, (2014); Walnut leaf extract inhibits PTP1B and enhances glucose-uptake *in vitro*; *J. Ethnopharmacol.*, 152(3), 599–602; doi: 10.1016/j.jep.2014.02.017

5. A. Santos, L. Barros, R.C. Calhelha, M. Dueñas, A.M. Carvalho, C. Santos-Buelga, I.C.F.R. Ferreira, (2013); Leaves and decoction of *Juglans regia* L.: Different performances regarding bioactive compounds and in vitro antioxidant and antitumor effects; *Ind. Crops Prod.*, 51, 430–6; doi: 10.1016/j.indcrop.2013.10.003

6. http://www.britannica.com/art/Queen-Anne-style [Accessed 04.09.16]

7. P. Brown, (25th April 2011); http://www.theguardian.com/environment/2011/apr/25/specieswatch-english-persian-walnut [Accessed 04.09.16]

8. M. Bol, (02.06.15); Clear as Crystal: Leonardo da Vinci's Walnut Oil, http://recipes.hypotheses.org/5806 [Accessed 04.09.16]

9. M.P. Strugstad, S. Despotovski, (2012); A Summary of Extraction, Synthesis, Properties, and Potential Uses of Juglone: A Literature Review; *Journal of Ecosystems and Management*, 13(3); http://jem.forrex.org/index.php/jem/article/viewFile/119/473 [Accessed 05.09.16]

10. D. Myers (2013); The Color of Art Pigments Database; http://www.artiscreation.com/brown.html#NBr7 [Accessed 05.09.16]

# Cherry Plum

## (*Prunus cerasifera*)

Cherry plum is a parent of the hybrid domesticated plum (*Prunus domestica*). The other parent may be *Prunus spinosa*, the sloe or blackthorn. In the UK, sloes are best known for their use in sloe gin. The fruit tends to be quite sour but it is edible. Both sloes and dried wild plums formed part of the diet of Ötzi the Iceman.[1] Ötzi's body was found on the Austrian/Italian border in 1991, frozen since about 3,200 BCE. Study of Ötzi's remains and possessions have given scientists and archaeologists a snapshot of life in the area over 5,000 years ago.

Cherry plum trees are among the first to flower in spring. The plums are about the size of cherries and are often used to make jam or fermented to make wine. When jam is made, the fruit is gently boiled, releasing pectin from the cell walls.[2,3] Pectin occurs in the skin and core of the fruit, where it helps form the structure. It was first isolated in 1825 by the chemist

**Cherry Plum** is the Bach flower remedy for those who fear losing control.

Henri Braconnot and consists of long chains of sugar molecules. Table sugar is then added to the fruit and this interacts with the water molecules present which would otherwise inhibit pectin chains from bonding to each other. Acid (in the form of lemon juice, mainly citric acid) is also added to reduce ionisation of the pectin chains to form carboxylate groups which would repel each other. When pectin chains bond to each other a gel is formed which traps the liquid and causes the jam to set. The pectin network forms at 104°C, the setting point of the jam. As well as sweetening the jam and helping it set, sugar also acts as a preservative by keeping the water content too low for microbes to grow.

Pectin (from the Greek *pektikos*, meaning congealing) is used as a gelling agent, thickener and stabiliser for other foods, in the pharmaceutical industry as a carrier for drugs and was used to treat diarrhoea.[4] It can help maintain normal blood cholesterol levels and reduce the rise in blood glucose levels after meals.[5] Modified citrus pectin (MCP), obtained by chemically modifying pectin from the peel and pulp of citrus fruits, has been shown to disrupt the spread of cancer cells. It has been suggested as a potential cancer treatment either alone or alongside conventional chemotherapy to improve the efficacy.[6] Pectin readily forms compounds with metal ions in the body and can facilitate the removal of problematic heavy metals such as cadmium, lead and arsenic by excretion of metal-pectin complexes in urine. Removal

of radioactive caesium by this method has also been demonstrated in children affected by the Chernobyl nuclear accident.[7]

Pectin also had a role to play in the printing of maps on silk for POWs during World War II.[8] These were developed by Christopher Clayton-Hutton, working for MI9. He had an interest in magic and escapology and famously bet Harry Houdini that he would not be able to escape from a crate made by the Clayton-Hutton family's timber company. Houdini won the bet, supposedly after bribing the carpenter to fit nails that would allow one panel to be easily removed from the inside. Clayton-Hutton developed maps printed on silk which survived wear and tear, could be easily concealed and also viewed silently without rustling. However, the ink tended to smear and it was not until he added pectin to prevent this that the level of detail required on the maps was produced.[8] Maps were sewn into airmen's clothing or included with the escape tools sent to POW camps concealed in items in care packages, possibly including Monopoly sets. The sets reportedly also contained files, a compass and local currency.[9]

Seeds and leaves of many species in the genus *Prunus*, including plums and apricots, contain the compound amygdalin. Amygdalin is sometimes known as laetrile, but laetrile is more correctly a hydrolysis product of amygdalin in which –COOH replaces

–CH$_2$–glucose. Laetrile/amygdalin is sometimes known as vitamin B17 although it is not actually a vitamin. Amygdalin was isolated in 1830 and first used as a cancer treatment in Russia in 1845. Its use in the USA began in the 1920s.[10] However, amygdalin metabolises in the human gut to produce sugar, benzaldehyde and hydrogen cyanide, a potent toxin. This has led to some cases of cyanide poisoning among patients. Amygdalin was one part of the unsuccessful cancer treatment given to the actor Steve McQueen in Mexico in 1980.[11] A Cochrane review concluded it is too toxic and lacking enough evidence to support its use.[12] However, today it is still promoted by some people.[13,14]

## Chemical diagram

### Amygdalin

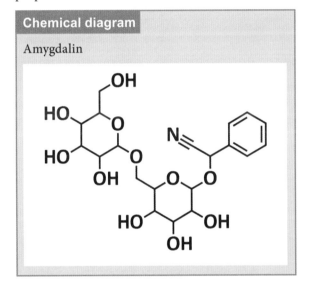

Hydrogen cyanide is also known as prussic acid and was first isolated from the pigment Prussian blue. It has a characteristic smell of almonds and is used as a starting material in the synthesis of many other chemical compounds and as a pesticide and fumigant. As a chemical warfare agent, it was reportedly used by Iraq in the 1980s and hydrogen cyanide was the main ingredient of Zyklon B which was used in Nazi gas chambers.[15] Hydrogen cyanide inhibits metal-containing enzymes in the body, including those linked to cell respiration.[16] Cyanide has been used for judicial executions in the US and in cases of murder or suicide. It was the poison used in Schrödinger's cat thought experiment, which would kill the cat if there was a decay of the radioactive substance in the box. The experiment, devised by Erwin Schrödinger in 1935, demonstrated concepts of quantum theory like superposition, where there appeared to be conflict between what is predicted at the microscopic level and what we can observe at the macroscopic level.[16]

The quantity of hydrogen cyanide produced by ingestion of plum seeds is unlikely to cause any harm. Assuming a fatal cyanide dose is 1.5 mg/kg body weight and that the reaction to produce cyanide gives 100% yield (of hydrogen cyanide plus benzaldehyde plus two molecules of glucose),[17] a 70 kg person would need to consume about 0.8 kg of plum seeds.

A recent ultra-conservative assessment gave a safe cyanide dose of 20 µg/kg body weight and suggested that consuming two or less small apricot stones a day was safe for adults[18] (apricots have about 6.5 times more amygdalin than plums).[17] However, if taking apricot pits for cancer treatment, the recommended intake is between 10 and 50 stones per day, a dose which might result in cyanide poisoning based on this assessment.[13] Symptoms of cyanide poisoning include stomach cramps, headache, vomiting and in serious cases, cardiac arrest, respiratory failure, coma and death.[17]

Benzaldehyde, also produced from amygdalin, is used in the food and cosmetics industries to give an almond flavour or scent.

**References:**

1. A. Fleckinger; Ötzi, the Iceman The Full Facts at a Glance; Folio Vienna/Bolzano, Third Updated Edition 2011, ISBN 978-3-85256-574-3, p 98

2. A. Brunning; What Makes Jam Set? – The Chemistry of Jam-Making; Compound Interest; http://www.compoundchem.com/2014/09/22/what-makes-jam-set-the-chemistry-of-jam-making/ [Accessed 10.09.16]

3. A. Connelly, (3rd October 2013); The science and magic of jam-making; The Guardian; https://www.theguardian.com/science/blog/2013/oct/03/science-magic-jam-making [Accessed 08.09.16]

4. P. Srivastava, R. Malviya, (2011); Sources of pectin, extraction and its applications in pharmaceutical industry – An overview; *Indian J. Nat. Prod. Resour.*, 2(1), 10–8; http://nopr.niscair.res.in/handle/123456789/11534 [Accessed 08.08.17]

5. European Food Safety Authority Panel on Dietetic Products, Nutrition and Allergies, (2010); *EFSA Journal*, 8(10), 1747; doi: 10.2903/j.efsa.2010.1747

6. V.V. Glinsky, A. Raz, (2009); Modified citrus pectin anti-metastatic properties: one bullet, multiple targets; *Carbohydr. Res.*, 344(14), 1788–91; doi: 10.1016/j.carres.2008.08.038

7. https://www.drugs.com/npp/pectin.html#ref7 [Accessed 10.09.16]

8. History of WWII British Cloth Escape Maps; http://www.escape-maps.com/escape_maps/history_of_wwii_british_cloth_escape_maps.htm#A._MI_9_and_Clayton_Hutton [Accessed 09.08.17]

9. C. Donlan, (12.01.14); Inside Monopoly's secret war against the Third Reich; Eurogamer.net; http://www.eurogamer.net/articles/2014-01-12-inside-monopolys-secret-war-against-the-third-reich [Accessed 10.09.16]

10. PubMed Health PDQ Cancer Information Summaries, (15th March 2017); Laetrile/Amygdalin Health Professional Version; https://www.ncbi.nlm.nih.gov/pubmedhealth/PMH0032851/ [Accessed 08.08.17]

11. B.H. Lerner, (15th November 2005); McQueen's Legacy of Laetrile; New York Times Health; http://www.nytimes.com/2005/11/15/health/mcqueens-legacy-of-laetrile.html [Accessed 10.09.16]

12. S. Milazzo, M. Horneber, (2015); Laetrile treatment for cancer; *Cochrane Database Syst. Rev.*, Issue 4, Art. No.: CD005476; doi: 10.1002/14651858.CD005476.pub4

13. The role of vitamin B17 in the fight against cancer; http://www.anticancerinfo.co.uk/index.html [Accessed 10.09.16]

14. Oasis of Hope Hospital; http://www.oasisofhope.com/cancer-treatments-therapies/laetrile/ [Accessed 10.09.16]

15. Organisation for the Prohibition of Chemical Weapons; Hydrogen Cyanide; https://www.opcw.org/about-chemical-weapons/types-of-chemical-agent/blood-agents/hydrogen-cyanide/ [Accessed 10.09.16]

16. A.M. Hernández; Hydrogen Cyanide from Prussian Blue to Schrödinger's Cat; http://www.chm.bris.ac.uk/motm/HCN/HCN.htm [Accessed 10.09.16]

17. The Guardian, (11th October 2015); Cyanide in fruit seeds: how dangerous is an apple?; https://www.theguardian.com/technology/2015/oct/11/cyanide-in-fruit-seeds-how-dangerous-is-an-apple [Accessed 11.09.16]

18. European Food Safety Authority, (22nd April 2015); Acute health risks related to consumption of raw apricot kernels and products thereof; Joint EFSA-EFET-BfR document; https://www.efsa.europa.eu/sites/default/files/4424ax1.pdf [Accessed 14.05.17]

# Crab Apple

(*Malus sylvestris*)

Related to domesticated apples, crab apple trees have a longer flowering period so are sometimes planted in commercial orchards as pollination partners. Their bark can become gnarled and twisted and this 'crabbed' appearance may have earned them their name. There are many varieties of apple but typically, crab apple fruits are smaller and more sour than domesticated apples. Fruit can be made into a jelly and crab apples are sometimes added during cider-making to make the resulting cider less sweet. A primitive form of cider was drunk by the Celtic Britons but production was first documented in the 13th century. In the 14th century, children were sometimes baptised using cider as this was cleaner than water. In some areas, the wages of farm workers included up to 8 pints of cider a day. This practice, called truck, was deemed illegal in 1887.[1]

Drinking or dry cider was thought to help rheumatism and gout and in regions where this cider was commonly consumed, levels of calculus were reportedly very low. Calculus is composed of solid mineral salts occurring in the body. Examples of calculus are kidney stones, gallstones and dental tartar. English diarist and intellectual John Evelyn wrote in 1664 that 'Generally all strong and pleasant cider excites and cleanses the Stomach, strengthens Digestion, and infallibly frees the Kidneys and Bladder from breeding the Gravel Stone'.[1] Today, with increased awareness of the negative effects of alcohol, apple cider vinegar (ACV) is promoted for its health benefits instead of cider. Producing ACV involves a second

**Crab Apple** is the Bach flower remedy for those who have feelings of self-disgust. It is the cleansing remedy.

fermentation, during which alcohol is converted to acetic acid (vinegar) by bacteria (usually *Acetobacter aceti*).

Traditionally, ACV was used as a disinfectant and Hippocrates used it to promote wound-healing.[2] Some studies have shown beneficial effects in reducing blood sugar levels in type 2 diabetics,[3] while other studies have shown no effect.[4] Other potential benefits include in reducing cholesterol, protecting against certain types of cancer and increasing feelings of fullness so aiding weight loss.[2] Excessive use can, however, have side effects such as throat and skin burns and the erosion of tooth enamel.[5] The use of ACV is sometimes suggested to remove dental tartar but, due to its detrimental effect on enamel, it should be rinsed off with plain water immediately after use.[6] Other suggested uses include to repel pet fleas, condition hair, soothe sunburn, balance the pH of skin and increase the pH in the digestive system.[7] This latter idea is exploited in a chewing gum, GutsyGum™, containing ACV (as well as calcium carbonate, liquorice extract and papain, from papaya) that reduces pain caused by gastro-intestinal reflux.[8]

Apple fruit contains acids including malic, gallic and tartaric acids. These can be beneficial to the liver and not only make the apple digestible but also render other foods more easily digested; fatty foods such as pork and cheese are often paired with apple. Malic acid got its name from the genus name *Malus*, although it does occur in fruits not in this genus including cherries, peaches and tomatoes. It is sometimes taken as a food supplement by people suffering from fibromyalgia and chronic fatigue syndrome to reduce muscle pain and increase energy. It is an ingredient of some skincare products, acting as an exfoliator and pH adjustor. In the food industry, it is used as a flavour enhancer and to mask unnatural tastes, such as those of artificial sweeteners.[9]

Ripe fruits can be eaten for constipation, while the verjuice (from unripe fruits) is taken for diarrhoea. A traditional remedy for warts involved rubbing the wart with two halves of an apple, after which the apple was buried. The wart supposedly disappeared as the apple decayed.

The origin of the word paradise may be in the Persian word *pardes* meaning orchard or park which then entered biblical Hebrew.[10] Apple trees are a symbol of fruitfulness, prosperity and rejuvenation and a good crop of apples is actively encouraged by wassailing. This originally took place on the old twelfth night (17th January), when locals would drink and sing to the trees. The aims were to scare off evil spirits and encourage benevolent spirits to ensure a good harvest of apples later in the year. Traditionally, a piece of cider-soaked toast was placed in the fork of the tree to attract good spirits![11]

When the inside of the fruit is exposed to air, the enzyme polyphenol oxidase (PPO) oxidises phenolic compounds to o-quinones which in turn produce brown pigments called melanins. These are responsible for a brown discolouration of apple flesh. The process can be avoided if the fruit is cooked,

deactivating the enzyme. Alternatively, apple pieces can be placed in water or coated with syrup or honey, limiting the amount of oxygen available. The pieces can also be exposed to acid (*e.g.* citric acid from lemon juice) to keep the pH too low for the enzymatic reaction to occur.[12] It is possible to genetically modify apples to turn off PPO production and so reduce browning. The resulting so-called Arctic apples became available in the US in the form of slices in 2017.[13] The apples will still brown when subject to bacterial or fungal infection (this type of browning occurs by a different process) but not because of superficial damage like bruising. Thus, it may be easier to tell if an apple is fit to eat.[13]

Like plum seeds, apple seeds (or pips) contain amygdalin, which produces hydrogen cyanide in the body (see cherry plum section for more details). Crab apples are also a good source of pectin which can be used

to help set jams (see cherry plum section for more details). The wood makes good quality timber and is also sometimes used for carving or turning. A yellow dye can be made using the bark.

Some people are allergic to apples because of Oral Allergy Syndrome (OAS, also known as Pollen Food Syndrome, PFS).[14] This can occur in people who have hay-fever due to the similarity of some of the proteins in pollen from trees, grasses and weeds with those in some fruit and vegetables. In northern latitudes, the Bet v1 protein in birch pollen is the major cause of hay-fever and sufferers can become sensitised to a protein in apples. Many other fruits and vegetables can cause a reaction including kiwi, celery, nectarines and apricots.[15] Symptoms are usually confined to the mouth and throat and occur within a few minutes of eating the fruit. The allergens involved can be deactivated by cooking, processing or digestion. OAS involving birch pollen can also cause allergy to soya milk, which contains high levels of a similar protein.[14] Other pollens implicated in OAS come from ragweed, mugwort and grasses. OAS may also be suffered by those who are allergic to natural rubber latex.[15]

Many health claims have been made for apples, some of which have been proven; there is some truth in the saying, 'An apple a day keeps the doctor away'. Some of the benefits come from compounds with strong antioxidant activities such as quercetin, phloretin and phlorizin (the 2'-glucoside of phloretin). Apples have been shown to inhibit cancer-cell proliferation, decrease lipid oxidation and lower cholesterol. However, the phytochemical composition of apples varies greatly between different varieties and there are also changes in composition during maturation and ripening of the fruit.[16]

Phloretin is found in the leaves, root bark and fruit and is sometimes used in anti-ageing skin products. Here it helps protect against the effects of UV-radiation by neutralising any free-radicals formed.[17] Both phloretin and phlorizin inhibit the transport of glucose in the body, with phlorizin the more effective of the two.[18] Phlorizin acts as an SGLT2 (sodium-glucose transport protein 2) inhibitor and was at one time considered as a potential drug to treat type 2 diabetes. However, it is poorly absorbed orally. It promotes excretion of glucose in the urine, excessive urination

and weight loss.[19] The study of phlorizin led to the development of synthetic analogues such as dapagliflozin and canagliflozin which are used today to treat the condition. They work by reducing the amount of glucose absorbed by the kidneys and the amount of glucose in the blood.[20]

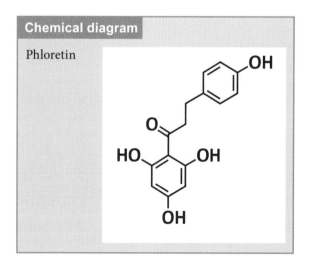

**Chemical diagram**

Phloretin

**References:**

1. http://cideruk.com/cider-lore/ [Accessed 09.08.17]

2. K. Gunnars, (5th September 2016); 6 Proven Benefits of Apple Cider Vinegar; https://authoritynutrition.com/6-proven-health-benefits-of-apple-cider-vinegar/ [Accessed 13.09.16]

3. *e.g.* A.M. White, C.S. Johnston, (2007); Vinegar Ingestion at Bedtime Moderates Waking Glucose Concentrations in Adults With Well-Controlled Type 2 Diabetes; *Diabetes Care*, 30(11), 2814–5; doi: 10.2337/dc07-1062

4. *e.g.* H.R. Nosrati, S.E. Mousavi, P. Sajjadi, A.R. Firoozjahi, Z. Moazezi, (2013); Effect of apple cider vinegar on postprandial blood glucose in type 2 diabetic patients treated with hypoglycemic agents; *J. Babol Univ. Med. Sci.*, 15(6), 7–11; http://jbums.org/article-1-4578-en.pdf

5. F. Spritzler; 7 Side Effects of Too Much Apple Cider Vinegar; https://authoritynutrition.com/

apple-cider-vinegar-side-effects/ [Accessed 13.09.16]

6. (4th March 2015); 3 Secret Techniques to Remove Plaque from Your Teeth At Home; http://www.thenaturalhealthmarket.co.uk/blog/3-secret-techniques-to-remove-plaque-from-your-teeth-at-home#sthash.yaCJfbIl.dpuf [Accessed 13.09.16]

7. L. Mitchell, (21st August 2012); 15 Reasons to Use Apple Cider Vinegar Every Day; http://www.mindbodygreen.com/0-5875/15-Reasons-to-Use-Apple-Cider-Vinegar-Every-Day.html [Accessed 13.09.16]

8. R. Brown, C.H.Y. Sam, T. Green, S. Wood, (2015); Effect of GutsyGum™, A Novel Gum, on Subjective Ratings of Gastro Esophageal Reflux Following A Refluxogenic Meal; *J. Diet. Suppl.*, 12(2), 138–45; doi: 10.3109/19390211.2014.950783

9. http://acidpedia.org/malic_acid/ [Accessed 14.09.16]

10. Balashon – Hebrew Language Detective, (28th December 2007); pardes and paradise; http://www.balashon.com/2007/12/pardes-and-paradise.html [Accessed 13.09.16]

11. http://www.historic-uk.com/CultureUK/Wassailing/ [Accessed 10.08.17]

12. Scientific American, (30th July 2007); Why do apple slices turn brown after being cut?; http://www.scientificamerican.com/article/

experts-why-cut-apples-turn-brown/ [Accessed 15.09.16]

13. http://www.arcticapples.com/arctic-apples-r/introducing-nonbrowning/ [Accessed 15.09.16]

14. https://www.anaphylaxis.org.uk/wp-content/uploads/2015/06/Pollen-Food-Syndrome-version-9-August-2016-1.pdf [Accessed 09.08.17]

15. J. Breeze; Foods That May Trigger Pollen Allergies; http://www.webmd.com/allergies/features/oral-allergy-syndrome-foods [Accessed 14.09.16]

16. J. Boyer, R.H. Liu, (2004); Apple phytochemicals and their health benefits; *Nutr. J.*, 3:5; doi: 10.1186/1475-2891-3-5

17. http://www.skinceuticals.com/phloretin-cf-635494328004.html [Accessed 15.09.16]

18. S.S. Chan, W.D. Lotspeich, (1962); Comparative effects of phlorizin and phloretin on glucose transport in the cat kidney; *Am. J. Physiol.*, 203, 975–9; http://ajplegacy.physiology.org/content/203/6/975

19. E.A.M. Gale, (12th November 2014); Phlorizin [internet]; Diapedia 8105429814 rev. no. 9; doi: 10.14496/dia.8105429814.9

20. https://www.diabetes.org.uk/Guide-to-diabetes/Managing-your-diabetes/Treating-your-diabetes/Tablets-and-medication/SGLT2-inhibitors/ [Accessed 09.08.17]

# Larch

## (*Larix decidua*)

Native to central Europe, larch was introduced into the UK in the 17th century and grown for timber. Larch wood is hard and resistant to rot so is used in fences, gates, staircases and garden furniture.

The bark of larch trees contains larixinic acid, more commonly known today as maltol. It is also found in pine needles and malt and is used in the food, beverage, pharmaceutical and cosmetics industries as a flavour enhancer. Maltol has the odour of caramel and butterscotch and is used in baked goods, confectionary and soft drinks. Use of maltol can enhance the sweet flavour of food so reducing the quantity of sugar required. For commercial use, it can be prepared synthetically.[1]

Ethyl maltol occurs naturally in cocoa, coffee and malt and can also be made from maltol. It has the aroma of toffee, caramel and fudge with a scent estimated to be 500 times more intense than maltol. In perfumery, it is used in the fragrance Thierry Mugler Angel and in some other sweet-smelling perfumes. More recently it has become a popular flavouring agent for e-cigarette liquid (as is maltol) and it is also used in the food industry.[2]

Maltol has a high affinity for metal ions and is well tolerated by the body.[3] It can therefore be useful medicinally either to deliver metal ions to, or remove them from, the body.

Iron deficiency, or anaemia, is a common condition and treatment can be challenging because iron is toxic at about five times the required concentration.

**Larch** is the Bach flower remedy for those who lack confidence.

Gastrointestinal side-effects of current treatments are common, leading to non-compliance.[3] However, maltol forms a complex with iron which has favourable properties; it is neutral, soluble and releases Fe(III) in the body. As the iron is readily bioavailable, the required dose of the complex is relatively low and this can reduce gastrointestinal problems.[4] A ferric-maltol drug is available and is used to treat iron-deficiency in patients with inflammatory bowel disease.[5]

The complex bis(maltato)-oxo-vanadium(IV) (BMOV) was the first purpose-designed vanadium-based insulin-enhancing agent for the treatment of type 2 diabetes. Compared to another possible vanadium-based drug, $VO(SO_4)$, BMOV has a two to three times stronger insulin-enhancing effect, lower incidence of gastrointestinal side-effects and a lower incidence of hypoglycaemic mortality. However, a further increase in potency and lower toxicity at higher doses would be beneficial, so study of related complexes is ongoing.[3] BMOV is under development as a drug for the treatment of heart attacks, targeting limitation of the area of tissue death. It also has possible uses for the reduction of tissue damage in burns cases and a reduction in reperfusion injury (damage caused to tissues when blood supply is restored after a break) in patients with acute kidney failure.[6] Other potential uses include for the treatment of strokes[6] and to promote healing of fractures.[7] These rely on the ability of BMOV to help keep traumatised but healthy cells alive and stimulate tissue repair[6] *via* an insulin-mediated pathway.[7]

Due to the similar coordination chemistry of Al(III) and Fe(III), maltol was studied as a potential agent to remove Al(III) ions from the brain. Accumulation of Al(III) in the brain is linked to oxidative stress which might lead to the development of Alzheimer's

disease and other conditions.[8] However, its neutral charge, high solubility and stability mean that the maltol complex is highly neurotoxic. There is, in fact, enhanced uptake of Al(III) in the presence of maltol and this has been used to induce Al(III) neurotoxicity in animals for experimental study.[3]

Maltol has antioxidant and anti-inflammatory activity and this may be behind its ability to reduce alcohol-related liver damage in mice.[9]

| Chemical diagram | |
| --- | --- |
| Maltol (larixinic acid) | 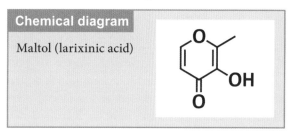 |

Larch is a source of arabinogalactan, a starch-like polymer made up of arabinose and galactose units. For commercial use, arabinogalactan is obtained from the bark of western larch (*Larix occidentalis*) or eastern larch (*Larix laricina*), although it also occurs in other larches. Extraction is eco-friendly, using hot water but no other solvents. Larch arabinogalactan (larch AG) is a prebiotic and, as it ferments in the intestine, increases favourable intestinal bacteria, promotes the production of short-chain fatty acids and reduces colon pH. It is sometimes taken to treat digestive problems and is used in the food industry as a stabiliser and binder, helping food retain water and flavour.[10] Larch AG also boosts the response of the immune system.[11] Specifically, it enhances the activity of so-called natural killer (NK) cells. These NK cells kill tumour cells and virus-infected cells. An increased activity of NK cells is a marker of good health. In a clinical trial, people taking larch AG were found to be 23% less likely to be infected with the common cold than those taking a placebo.[12] Larch AG is sometimes used to treat respiratory conditions, swine flu, HIV, middle-ear infection, liver disease and cancer, to reduce cholesterol and to boost the immune system.[13]

Venice turpentine is obtained from the heart of the

larch tree. In contrast, other turpentines come from tree barks.[14] It is used in veterinary medicine as a disinfectant and antibacterial agent, particularly for the treatment of horses' hooves. Treatment with the turpentine forms a barrier to moisture, toughening the soles. Acting as a counter-irritant, it inflames the skin and stimulates healing of the underlying muscles and tendons and promotes new hoof growth.[15] It was traditionally used in humans to treat hospital gangrene. Valued for the absence of abietic acid crystals which discolour other turpentines, it is sometimes used by artists in oil painting, giving an enamel-like gloss. The honey-coloured resin was used historically for making varnishes.[14] The name Venice turpentine may allude to the use of larch wood (along with elm, alder and oak) in the construction of Venice.

Larch is the source of Briançon manna — a white, sugary substance produced as oblong 'tears' by aphids eating the sap in summer. Sometimes known as European false manna, it does not contain any mannitol (mannite), the main component of manna obtained from the manna tree (flowering ash, *Fraxinus ornus*). The major sugar component of Briançon manna, also known as honeydew, is melezitose. The honeydew

attracts ants which may protect the aphids against predators. The ants also maintain hygiene by removing residual honeydew.[16] A high melezitose content is suggested as the main factor in the formation of cement honey. This crystallised honey, first reported by beekeepers in Poland in 2002, contains 10 times as much melezitose as normal honey.[17]

In traditional medicine, the inner bark of larch was used externally to treat eczema and psoriasis and internally to treat haemorrhages and cystitis. It was also used as a stimulant expectorant for chronic bronchitis. The wearing or burning of larch was thought to protect against evil spirits.

Larch trees are deciduous, shedding their needles every year. Before this happens, they turn a characteristic yellow colour and this feature was utilised in the 1930s when the Nazis planted larch trees to form a swastika shape in an evergreen pine forest. The 200-foot swastika, visible only from the air, was located in 1992. First attempts to remove it were unsuccessful, after the larch trees regrew and there were disputes over property ownership. However, German authorities removed 25 of the trees in 2000, finally disrupting the symbol, fearing the site in Brandenburg Forest might become a rallying point for neo-Nazis.[18]

### References:

1. https://noshly.com/additive/636/flavour-enhancer/636/ [Accessed 12.08.17]

2. Chemist in the Bottle, (24th April 2014); Maltol and Ethyl Maltol; https://chemistinthebottle. wordpress.com/2014/04/24/chemistry-flash-maltol-and-ethyl-maltol/ [Accessed 23.09.16]

3. K.H. Thompson, C.A. Barta, C. Orvig, (2006); Metal complexes of maltol and close analogues in medicinal inorganic chemistry; *Chem. Soc. Rev.*, 35(6), 545–56; doi: 10.1039/B416256K

4. S.M. Kelsey, R.C. Hider, J.R. Bloor, D.R. Blake, C.N. Gutteridge, A.C. Newland, (1991); Absorption of low and therapeutic doses of ferric maltol, a novel ferric iron compound, in iron-deficient subjects using a single dose iron absorption test; *J. Clin. Pharm. Ther.*, 16(2), 117–22; doi: 10.1111/j.1365-2710.1991.tb00292.x

5. http://www.shieldtherapeutics.com/product/feraccru/ [Accessed 24.09.16]

6. http://cfmpharma.com/the-new-drug-vanadis/ [Accessed 24.09.16]

7. S.S. Lin, D.N. Paglia, J.P. O'Connor, E. Breitbart, J. Benevenia, (priority date 15.01.2010); Use of vanadium compounds to accelerate bone healing; *European Patent*, EP2523672

8. M.F. van Ginkel, G.B. van der Voet, P.C. D'Haese, M.E. De Broe, F.A. de Wolff, (1993); Effect of citric acid and maltol on the accumulation of aluminium in rat brain and bone; *J. Lab. Clin. Med.*, 121(3), 453–60; http://www.translationalres.com/ article/0022-2143(93)90281-3/pdf

9. Y. Han, Q. Xu, J.-N. Hu, X.-Y. Han, W. Li, L.-C. Zhao, (2015); Maltol, a Food Flavoring Agent, Attenuates Acute Alcohol-Induced Oxidative Damage in Mice; *Nutrients*, 7(1), 682–96; doi: 10.3390/nu7010682

10. A. Fitzpatrick, A. Roberts, S. Witherly, (2004); Larch arabinogalactan: A novel and multifunctional natural product; *Agro Food Ind. Hi Tech*, 15(1), 30–2; http://www.teknoscienze.com/agro/pdf/ larch_arabinoglactan.....pdf

11. C. Dion, E. Chappuis, C. Ripoll, (2016); Does larch arabinogalactan enhance immune function? A review of mechanistic and clinical trials; *Nutr. Metab. (Lond.)*, 13, 28; doi: 10.1186/s12986-016-0086-x

12. L. Riede, B. Grube, J. Gruenwald (2013); Larch arabinogalactan effects on reducing incidence of upper respiratory infections; *Curr. Med. Res. Opin.*, 29(3), 251–8; doi: 10.1185/03007995.2013.765837

13. http://www.webmd.com/vitamins-supplements/ ingredientmono-974-larch%20arabinogalactan.aspx? activeingredientid=974& [Accessed 27.09.16]

14. http://www.atlantisart.co.uk/ roberson-larch-venice-turpentine/ [Accessed 28.09.16]

15. E. Blazer, (2014); Venice Turpentine; The Way of Horses; http://www.thewayofhorses.com/ 10_14_venice_turpentine.html [Accessed 28.09.16]

16. I. Yao, (2014); Costs and constraints in aphid-ant mutualism; *Ecol. Res.*, 29(3), 383–91; doi: 10.1007/s11284-014-1151-4

17. T. Szczęsna, H. Rybak-Chmielewska, P. Skubida, (2003); Contribution to the understanding of "cement" honey; *J. Apic. Sci.*; 47(2), 103–8; http://www.jas.org.pl/Contribution-to-the- understanding-of-the-phenomenon-of-cement- honey,0,242.html

18. D. Kringiel, (5th July 2013); The Mystery of the Forest Swastikas; Spiegel Online; http://www.spiegel.de/ international/germany/mystery-of-nazi-swastikas-in-the- forests-a-909726.html [Accessed 28.09.16]

Larches in autumn

# Olive

## (*Olea europaea*)

In many cultures, olive trees and olive oil were considered sacred. The olive branch was a symbol of abundance, glory and peace. Moses considered workers who cultivated olives so important that he exempted them from military service. The leafy branches were ritually offered to deities and powerful figures as emblems of benediction and purification. Branches were found in Tutankhamun's tomb. Olive oil was used to anoint kings and athletes in ancient Greece and was termed 'liquid gold' by Homer. It was burnt in the sacred lamps of temples and to produce the 'eternal flame' of the original Olympic Games. Victors in these Games were crowned with its leaves. Today, olive oil is still used in many religious ceremonies. The flag of the United Nations shows the world viewed from the North Pole symbolically surrounded by olive branches.

The artist Pierre Auguste Renoir bought a house, Les Collettes, in south-eastern France where he spent the last 11 years of his life. The main reason for this purchase was that he didn't want the ancient olive grove attached to the house destroyed to make way for a proposed market garden. He attempted to paint the trees but struggled, saying they were full of colours, always changing and that the colour lay between the leaves and not on them. He said, "The olive tree, what a brute! If you realised how much trouble it caused me". Vincent van Gogh also painted at least 18 pictures of olive trees. In 2015, land artist Stan Herd reproduced one of them in a project funded by the Minneapolis Institute of Art (MIA) to celebrate

**Olive** is the Bach flower remedy for those suffering from exhaustion following mental or physical effort.

the museum's centenary. The work, based on the 1889 painting 'Olive Trees' which is on display in the museum, covered 1.2 acres near Minneapolis-St. Paul International Airport.[1]

Over 90% of olives are used for oil; the fruit is macerated, the stone removed and then the pulp is cold pressed to extract virgin olive oil. This has the best flavour and the highest cost. Subsequent pressings yield lower quality oils. These include refined olive oil which has been treated with charcoal and filtered and also olive pomace which is often used for cooking or in soap. The industry sometimes makes use of the stones, burning them to provide heat for processing.

Virgin oil is often adulterated with cheap oils such as canola or sunflower. Over 50% of extra virgin oil sold in Italy and about 80% of that sold in the USA is believed to be adulterated. The profit margin made on selling adulterated oil can be three times that made from the sale of cocaine. The process is under the control of organised crime, nicknamed the Agromafia.[2]

Extra virgin oil contains oleocanthal, a phenolic compound responsible for the burning sensation experienced when consuming the oil.[3] The name oleocanthal derives from *oleo*, olive, *canth* for burning and *al* denoting that the compound is an aldehyde. Oil quality is sometimes related to the pungency; one-cough oil is considered inferior to two-cough oil (containing more oleocanthal)! Adulterated oils have pepper or other substances added to reproduce the burning effect.

Oleocanthal has antioxidant and anti-inflammatory properties. It inhibits the COX enzymes so reduces pain and inflammation in the same manner as popular drugs like ibuprofen and aspirin do.[4] In fact, ibuprofen produces the same throat irritation as virgin olive oil containing oleocanthal does. Oleocanthal activates the TRPA1 receptor, the receptor for irritants and stench, also activated by compounds in garlic, onions and wasabi. Variation in the expression of this receptor in the oropharyngeal region (between the back of the nose and the epiglottis) may account for

**Chemical diagram**

Oleocanthal

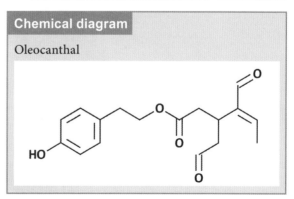

the observed differences in sensitivity to oleocanthal.[5]

50 g of oil contains enough oleocanthal to give a similar anti-inflammatory effect to one tenth of the adult dose of ibuprofen. It has been suggested that long-term consumption of small quantities may be responsible in part for the low incidence of heart disease and Alzheimer's disease associated with a Mediterranean diet. However, 50 g corresponds to 4 tablespoons of oil which is more than most consumers would ingest per day. In addition, the effects of oleocanthal in the human body are not yet fully understood.[6]

Oleocanthal also has potential benefit in the treatment of cancer, acting very quickly and targeting cancer cells rather than healthy ones.[7] It pierces the cancer cells' waste storage containers, or vesicles, releasing enzymes that cause cell death. Cancer cells are affected in under an hour while healthy cells only suffer a temporary halt to their life cycle and this returns to normal after 24 hours. Other suggested medicinal benefits are in the prevention of joint degenerative disease (osteoarthritis) and neuro-degenerative conditions.[3]

The potential health benefits of oleocanthal and other compounds in olives are such that, in 2015, a group of olive oil experts launched the Oleocanthal International Society. The organisation aims to encourage research into the properties of high-phenolic olive products and publicise the results.[8]

Olives also contain the omega-9 fatty acid oleic acid (the double bond involves the ninth carbon in the chain), present as a triglyceride. Although its name is related to olives, oleic acid is common in the human diet. It is also released by some types of caterpillars, cockroaches, woodlice and ants to signal that they're dead; they are then removed by their mates.[9] In an experiment carried out by Ed Wilson, a living ant which was daubed with oleic acid was dragged off by other ants for disposal as if it were dead. The ant repeatedly cleaned itself and tried to re-enter the colony only to be removed again until it was finally free of the 'I'm dead' smell after a couple of hours. When an ant dies, oleic acid is released after about two days.[10] As well as signalling that there is a dead ant to be removed, the smell might also indicate danger to living insects, prompting them to avoid ants who have succumbed to disease or places where predators may lurk.[9]

In traditional medicine, olive oil was used in plasters and ointments and to treat the lungs and bowels. It is a laxative, good for circulation and improves digestion. The leaves were used to disinfect wounds. Olive leaf teas were used to lower fevers and olive poultices were among the oldest known treatments for infections of the skin, cuts and bruises. Today, the oil is used in cooking, in skincare, as a massage oil and in haircare. Its use in skincare is supported by proven antioxidant properties. The oil contains vitamin E, mainly as α-tocopherol, and hydroxytyrosol which has been shown to protect cells against damage from UV-A

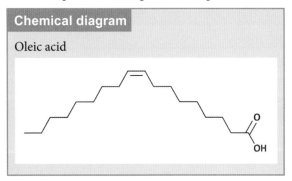

Chemical diagram

Oleic acid

light.[11] Olive oil can penetrate hair which makes it beneficial in maintaining the moisture balance in certain hair-types.[12] It is sometimes used as a home remedy for hair lice.

The age of olive trees can be difficult to determine by the usual method of counting tree rings due to their irregular formation. This is related to the lack of seasonality in parts of the Mediterranean where the trees grow. The trees' response to temperature variations can produce false rings and tree-ring boundaries can be difficult to identify.[13] However, carbon dating, measuring the decay of the radioactive isotope of carbon ($^{14}$C), has been used to estimate the age of an olive tree trunk in the Garden of Gethsemane, Israel, as about 900 years.[14] Some trees are claimed to be even older, approximately 1500 years old (and still producing olives!).

The related Asian fragrant olive, or tea olive (*Osmanthus fragrans*), produces peach-scented flowers which are used, as the tree's common name suggests, to flavour tea, wine and confectionary. The city of Guilin (meaning 'forest of sweet osmanthus') is named after the fragrant olives which are abundant there. Tea olive is a popular street tree in the warmer parts of China and it is also used in perfumery and herbal medicine.[15]

### References:

1. C. Jobson, (23rd September 2015); Artist Stan Herd Plants a 1.2-Acre Field Inspired by Van Gogh's 1889 Painting "Olive Trees"; http://www.thisiscolossal.com/2015/09/stand-herd-van-gogh-field/ [Accessed 21.10.16]

2. B. Whitaker, (3rd January 2016); Agromafia; http://www.cbsnews.com/news/60-minutes-agromafia-food-fraud/ [Accessed 21.10.16]

3. L. Parkinson, R. Keast, (2014); Oleocanthal, a Phenolic Derived from Virgin Olive Oil: A Review of the Beneficial Effects on Inflammatory Disease; *Int. J. Mol. Sci.*, 15(7), 12323–34; doi: 10.3390/ijms150712323

4. G.K. Beauchamp, R.S.J. Keast, D. Morel, J. Lin, J. Pika, Q. Han, C.-H. Lee, A.B. Smith, P.A.S. Breslin, (2005); Phytochemistry: Ibuprofen-like activity in extra-virgin olive oil; *Nature*, 437, 45–6; doi: 10.1038/437045a

5. C. Peyrot des Gachons, K. Uchida, B. Bryant, A. Shima, J.B. Sperry, L. Dankulich-Nagrudny, M. Tominaga, A.B. Smith, G.K. Beauchamp, P.A.S. Breslin, (2011); Unusual pungency from extra-virgin olive oil is attributable to restricted spatial expression of the receptor of oleocanthal; *J. Neurosci.*, 31(3), 999–1009; doi: 10.1523/JNEUROSCI.1374-10.2011

6. M. Hopkin, (31st August 2005); Extra-virgin olive oil mimics painkiller; http://www.nature.com/drugdisc/news/articles/050829-11.html [Accessed 21.10.16]

7. N. Lavars, (19th February 2015); Olive oil ingredient leads cancer cells to their death; http://www.gizmag.com/olive-oil-ingredient-cancer-cell-death/36180/ [Accessed 22.10.16]

8. A. Gadanidis, (11th June 2015); An International Society for Oleocanthal; http://www.oliveoiltimes.com/olive-oil-health-news/oleocanthal-international-society/47974 [Accessed 22.10.16]

9. M. Walker, (9th September 2009); Ancient 'smell of death' revealed; http://news.bbc.co.uk/earth/hi/earth_news/newsid_8232000/8232607.stm [Accessed 21.10.16]

10. R. Krulwich, (1st April 2009); 'Hey I'm Dead!' The Story Of The Very Lively Ant; http://www.npr.org/sections/krulwich/2009/04/01/102601823/hey-im-dead-the-story-of-the-very-lively-ant [Accessed 21.10.16]

11. S. D'Angelo, D. Ingrosso, V. Migliardi, A. Sorrentino, G. Donnarumma, A. Baroni, L. Masella, M.A. Tufano, M. Zappia, P. Galletti, (2005); Hydroxytyrosol, a natural antioxidant from olive oil, prevents protein damage induced by long-wave ultraviolet radiation in melanoma cells; *Free Radic. Biol. Med.*, 38(7), 908–19; doi: 10.1016/j.freeradbiomed.2004.12.015

12. (24th June 2013, Updated: June 2016); Oils — Which Ones Soak In vs. Coat the Hair?; http://science-yhairblog.blogspot.co.uk/2013/06/oils-which-ones-soak-in-vs-coat-hair.html [Accessed 22.10.16]

13. P. Cherubini, T. Humbel, H. Beeckman, H. Gärtner, D. Mannes, C. Pearson, W. Schoch, R. Tognetti, S. Lev-Yadun, (2013); Olive Tree-Ring Problematic Dating: A Comparative Analysis on Santorini (Greece); *PLoS ONE*, 8(1): e54730; doi: 10.1371/journal.pone.0054730

14. M. Davidson, (29th November 2013); Long-lived Olive Trees; http://epod.usra.edu/blog/2013/11/long-lived-olive-trees.html [Accessed 22.10.16]

15. http://www.kew.org/science-conservation/plants-fungi/osmanthus-fragrans-fragrant-olive [Accessed 21.10.16]

# Hornbeam

## (*Carpinus betulus*)

The name hornbeam means 'hard tree' and the hornbeams are sometimes known as ironwoods or musclewoods.[1] This hardness makes the wood difficult to work with but it was used to make ox-yokes. One common name of *Carpinus betulus* (common or European hornbeam) is yoke elm. The wood was also used to make cogs for windmills and water-wheels and butchers' chopping boards. The Romans sometimes built chariots using hornbeam wood. One suggestion for the origin of the tree's name is that *carpinus* comes from *carpentum*,[2] a two-wheeled carriage with an arched covering, made from hard wood. The wood was burned for fuel or charcoal and was traditionally used in bakers' ovens. Common hornbeam is often used in hedging. In mythology, ironwood trees are sometimes depicted as ladders between worlds and as sources of wisdom and life.[1]

There are over 30 species of hornbeam. Often misidentified as beech, the hornbeam can be distinguished by the double serrations of its deeply furrowed ('pleated') leaves. The bark is grey and is sinewy when mature, giving the tree a muscular appearance. Both male and female catkins are found on the same tree. After pollination, female catkins develop into papery, green winged fruits, known as samaras.

Japanese hornbeam (*Carpinus japonica*) is commonly grown in cities, where its short stature means it doesn't interfere with power lines and its light leaves are easily swept up so do not clog storm drains. It is sometimes pruned to form bonsai.[3] American

**Hornbeam** is the Bach flower remedy for those who are tired at the thought of what lies ahead. The remedy for the 'Monday-morning feeling'.

hornbeam (*Carpinus caroliniana*) is commonly known as blue beech and produces edible (though small) seeds. Only a single tree of the Puto hornbeam (sometimes Putuo hornbeam), *Carpinus putoensis*, remains in the wild, on Mount Putuo island near Shanghai in China. As the tree produces both male and female catkins it is still capable of reproducing, although critically endangered.[4] The island is an important site in Chinese Buddhism.

A tonic made from hornbeam is used to relieve both mental and physical tiredness. Externally, the leaves are used to staunch bleeding and help to heal wounds. An infusion made with the leaves is used to bathe the eyes to treat infections and relieve tiredness and puffiness.[5] It is also taken for toothache.[6] The inner bark is used as a purgative and the boiled bark to treat sore muscles and rheumatism. Hornbeam's stimulant properties have led to claims it can help reduce hair loss if taken internally or massaged into the scalp. Extracts are included in some products for hair loss.

It is also used to treat digestive and respiratory problems, hay-fever and allergies.[5]

The leaves of hornbeam contain pheophorbide-a which shows activity against some types of human cancer cells when exposed to a certain wavelength of light, using a technique called photodynamic therapy (PDT).[7] In PDT, the drug (photosensitiser) is only active after exposure to light. By targeting the light towards the area to be treated, damage to other cells can be minimised.

Initially, pheophorbide-a was thought to be preferentially found in older leaves, suggesting it is a product of the breakdown of chlorophyll.[7] However, it has been reported to be more abundant in young leaves which would refute this idea and suggests a physiological role for the compound, which is, as yet, unknown. There is a seasonal effect on the activity of the ethyl acetate leaf extracts of hornbeam, with lower activity in August and September than in spring. This may be related to the relative abundance of pheophorbide-a in spring. There are some problems with using the compound in PDT, however, including limited selectivity towards cancer cells, so derivatives are currently being tested.[8]

The antioxidant properties of hornbeam also vary throughout the year. The highest antioxidant capacities occur in August and May. The effect of the August extract may be the result of the high content of chlorogenic acid, ellagic acid, ellagitannins and myricetin-, luteolin-, quercetin- and apigenin glycosides. The compound(s) responsible for the high antioxidant capacity of the May extract have yet to be determined and work on this is ongoing. In all, 171 known and unknown compounds have been identified in the leaf extracts, including phenolic acids, tannins and flavonoid glycosides.[9]

The presence of tannins makes the bark astringent.[10] Tannins are common in plants and are often present in tree barks including in oak, chestnut and birch. They are classed as polyphenols and have variable composition. As they make the bark bitter, one role

**Samaras**

may be to protect it from predators. They have antimicrobial action and act as a chemical barrier to bacteria and fungi. They also act as an anti-freeze, protecting the tree from cold temperntures.[11] Tannins have the property of binding to certain organic molecules such as proteins and alkaloids. When milk is added to tea, the tannins in the tea leaves bind to proteins in the milk, reducing the binding of tannins to proteins in the body (*e.g.* in the liver and kidneys) after the tea is drunk.[10]

Tannins are primarily used to tan leather. They bind to collagen molecules in the hides, coating them and giving protection from water and bacteria. They also make the resulting leather more flexible.[10] Tannins from plants are of two types, namely hydrolysable or non-hydrolysable (condensed), depending on

**Chemical diagram**

Pheophorbide-a

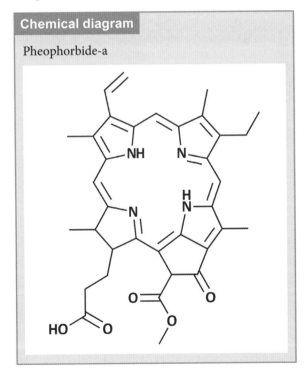

whether they react with water or not. Hydrolysable tannins give a paler tan colour but a harder-wearing, more water-resistant leather than non-hydrolysable tannins do.[11]

The simplest hydrolysable tannins are the gallotannins, formed by addition of between one and five gallic acid molecules to a central glucose molecule.[12] All five of these variations are found in hornbeam bark,[9] including pentagalloyl glucose (gallotannic acid) and multiple isomers of the others. Isomers are formed because there is more than one possible way the gallic acid molecules can be added to glucose, and these are not equivalent (glucose has five –OH groups and galloyl groups can replace any of the H's).

### Chemical diagram

Acertannin

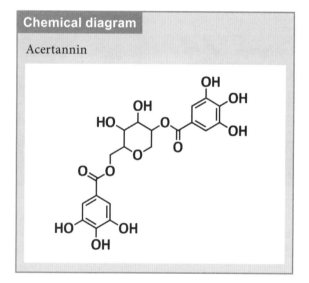

The gallic acid portions of the molecule can be further derivatised to give more complex structures, including the ellagitannins. The sugar can also be adapted, for example, by removal of water. An example of a digalloyl-1,5-anhydroglucitol isomer (with 2 groups from gallic acid and a modified sugar group) is acertannin (also known as aceritannin). Found in sugar maple (*Acer saccharum*), acertannin has antihyperglycaemic effects so may be useful for the treatment of diabetes.[13] Each tree species has its own individual mixture of tannins as well as a differing quantity of each. Tanners use different barks depending on the desired effect.

Tannins are also used to clarify beer and wine, to reduce the viscosity of drilling mud for oil wells, and in boiler water to prevent scale formation. Medicinally, they have been used to treat tonsillitis, pharyngitis, haemorrhoids and skin conditions. They have also been administered internally to check diarrhoea and intestinal bleeding and as an antidote for metallic, alkaloidal and glycosidic poisons, working by forming insoluble precipitates with the poisons.[14]

## References:

1. http://www.findyourfate.com/astrology/plants/trees/ironwood.html [Accessed 23.10.16]

2. F.G. Heath, (2012); Tree Lore (The Paranormal); David and Charles, Kindle Edition, p 65 (*via* Google Books)

3. http://www.2020site.org/trees/hornbeam.html [Accessed 23.10.16]

4. IUCN Red List, (2017-1); *Carpinus putoensis*, Puto Hornbeam; doi: 10.2305/IUCN.UK.2014-3.RLTS.T32303A2813038.en

5. http://www.home-remedies-for-you.com/herbs/hornbeam.html [Accessed 23.10.16]

6. http://connected-sustainability.org/portfolio_page/hornbeam/ [Accessed 22.10.16]

7. L.E. Xodo, V. Rapozzi, M. Zacchigna, S. Drioli, S. Zorzet, (2012); The Chlorophyll Catabolite Pheophorbide a as a Photosensitizer for the Photodynamic Therapy; *Curr. Med. Chem.*, 19(6), 799–807; doi: 10.2174/092986712799034879

8. E. Cieckiewicz, L. Angenot, T. Gras, R. Kiss, M. Frédérich, (2012); Potential anticancer activity of young *Carpinus betulus* leaves; *Phytomedicine*, 19(3–4), 278–83; doi: 10.1016/j.phymed.2011.09.072

9. T. Hofmann, E. Nebehaj, L. Albert, (2016); Antioxidant properties and detailed polyphenol profiling of European hornbeam (*Carpinus betulus* L.) leaves by multiple antioxidant capacity assays and high-performance liquid chromatography/multistage electrospray mass spectrometry; *Ind. Crops Prod.*, 87, 340–9; doi: 10.1016/j.indcrop.2016.04.037

10. M. Richards, (2000); Bark Tanning; https://braintan.com/barktan/1basics.htm [Accessed 22.10.16]

11. K. Palmer; Tannins and Tanning; https://www.woodland-ways.co.uk/blog/primitive-crafts/tannins-and-tanning/ [Accessed 27.10.16]

12. A.E. Hagerman, (2002, 2010); Hydrolyzable Tannin Structural Chemistry; http://www.users.miamioh.edu/hagermae/Hydrolyzable%20Tannin%20Structural%20Chemistry.pdf [Accessed 27.10.16]

13. A. Honma, T. Koyama, K. Yazawa, (2010); Anti-hyperglycemic effects of sugar maple *Acer saccharum* and its constituent acertannin; *Food Chem.*, 123(2), 390–4; doi: 10.1016/j.foodchem.2010.04.052

14. Encyclopaedia Britannica; https://www.britannica.com/topic/tannin

# Oak

*(Quercus robur)*

The common, English or pedunculate oak, *Quercus robur,* is native to Western Europe. Its perceived strength and longevity have made it a popular symbol; in the UK, the oak features in the logos of both the National Trust and the Conservative Party. Oaks can shorten in height as they age, to increase their lifespan. Common oaks have characteristic deeply-lobed leaves with smooth edges. They produce lammas shoots during the summer, initially golden and turning green. This means oaks retain strong leaves until late in the year. The nuts or acorns occur on long stalks (peduncles) which distinguishes the tree from the sessile oak (*Quercus petraea*), which produces acorns with no stalks. The nuts are held in a woody cup-like base.

Oak wood has been used for building, furniture-making and in shipbuilding. It also provided charcoal which burned hotly enough to smelt precious metals. Oak-framed houses are relatively flexible so can withstand earthquakes and tornadoes. When the Armada came to England in 1588, King Philip of Spain ordered that the Forest of Dean in Gloucestershire be burned down to destroy the oak trees, to prevent any more shipbuilding. Although Philip's order was never carried out, within 200 years most of the oak trees in the Forest had been cut down for timber; Admiral Nelson asked the Crown to replant it, along with other depleted oak woods. Nelson's ship HMS Victory was built using an estimated 5,000 oak trees.

Oak's attraction to shipbuilders was partly the tree's status in mythology. Connected to the gods Thor and

**Oak** is the Bach flower remedy for those who are strong and steady in character but carry on beyond the point of exhaustion.

Zeus, it was believed to be a fire and lightning charm and to possess magical as well as intrinsic strength. The species name *robur* is Latin for strength and robustness. Oak trees are said to be struck by lightning more often than other trees. This was believed to show that the trees were the channel through which the gods reached down to earth. However, as well as often being the tallest tree in the area, oak trees have a low electrical resistance due to their high moisture content, which possibly accounts for the attraction they have for lightning.

Legend has it that British king Charles II sheltered in an oak tree at Boscobel House after the Battle of Worcester in 1651, to escape his Parliamentary enemies. When he was restored to the throne in 1660, the date (29th May), which was also Charles' birthday, became a public holiday. It was observed as Royal Oak Day (or Oak Apple Day) and celebrated annually until 1859. On this date churches, houses and people were decorated with oak. Today, the date is still celebrated as Founder's Day at the Royal Chelsea Hospital, which was established by Charles in 1681.[1] Oak apples are a type of gall found on oak trees, often resembling the shape of an apple and about 2–4 cm in diameter.

Galls form when oak gall wasps (*e.g. Cynips quercusfolii*) lay their eggs on the tree. When the larvae hatch and begin to feed, they excrete an irritant substance and the oak responds by producing a gall *i.e.* an abnormal outgrowth of tissue. The gall provides food and protection for the larvae which exit the gall when they become wasps.

The Topless Oaks in Bradgate Park in Leicestershire were said to have been pollarded (*i.e.* the upper branches were removed) as a sign of mourning following the beheading of Lady Jane Grey in 1554. She had lived at the nearby Bradgate Hall and was a great-niece of King Henry VIII. She was briefly Queen of England, Ireland and France, but reigned for only nine days before being executed for treason.[2]

The Major Oak, in Sherwood Forest, Nottinghamshire, was said to have sheltered Robin Hood. He supposedly held meetings with his band of men within the hollow tree and sometimes also slept there. It still stands today, although it needs support to prevent it from collapsing. Believed to be between 800 and 1000 years old, the tree weighs 23 tonnes, has a girth of 10 metres and a spread of 28 metres, making it the biggest oak tree in Britain.[3] The Major Oak won England's Tree of the Year competition, run by the Woodland Trust, in 2014. It was originally known as Cockpen Tree as, in the 18th century, the hollow interior was used to pen cockerels ready to be used for cock-fighting. It became known as the Major Oak after Major Hayman Rooke included it in his book on oak trees in 1790.[4] The tree now stands on a protected site, but in 2002 some of its acorns were offered for sale illegally on the internet for £250 each.[5]

The mythical strength of oak translated into some of its traditional uses. Toothache sufferers sometimes hammered a nail into an oak tree, believing the tree would take away their pain! 'Lungs of oak' were taken by people with tuberculosis or chest complaints – this is actually a lichen, *Stricta pulmonaria* (or *Lobaria pulmonaria*), which resembles lungs and grows on some types of oak tree. Couples got married under oak trees, hoping to absorb the tree's strength and vitality. The bark of oak trees was also used to make

**Acorns**

love potions. The Druids were known as the wise men of oak, their name literally meaning those who know the oak. As oak has deep roots, oak remedies were used to heal weary feet and help them to find the right pathway through life.

A comparison of the leafing time of ash and oak was used in country-lore to foretell the coming weather,

'If the ash leafs before oak, we're in for a soak,
But if oak leafs before ash, we're in for merely a splash'.

Acorns were a traditional food for pigs and historically were eaten by peasants in times of famine. They were also ground and used as a coffee substitute. When used as pig food, acorns had to be mixed with other vegetable foods to counter their binding properties! A distilled spirit made from acorns was taken to help 'to control an abnormal craving for alcoholic liquor'. Oak bark was used to produce a brown dye; the names of the light brown colour tan or tawny come from the Latin *tannum* for oak bark.

Powdered bark was inhaled as a treatment for tuberculosis and tanners were almost immune to the disease. A remedial snuff made from the bark was also taken. Today, a decoction of the bark is used as a gargle for tonsillitis or laryngitis. It is used as an astringent *e.g.* for those suffering from diarrhoea, dysentery or haemorrhoids. Oak galls have the same effects and provide the strongest of all vegetable astringents.

**Oak seedling**

**Galls**

Gallotannic acid

This astringency has led to some health claims for the galls made by online sellers. In 2017, a listing on Etsy claimed they could be used by women after childbirth to restore elasticity to uterine walls, in a 'feminine wash' or to improve their sex lives. However, an expert has discounted these uses and highlighted their dangers.[6]

Oak galls can be used to produce iron gall ink, which was the most important writing material in the West from the Middle Ages to the 20th century. Gallotannic acid from the gall is mixed with water to produce gallic acid which is then reacted with vitriol (iron(II) sulfate) to produce the ink. Gum arabic, from acacia trees, is added as a suspension agent. The ink is soluble (as iron(II)) and light-coloured but darkens and becomes insoluble by oxidation (to iron(III)) when it is absorbed by the writing surface, making it permanent.[7] Aleppo galls from *Quercus infectoria*, Aleppo oak, contain the greatest amount of gallotannic acid (over 50%) while galls from the common oak contain 15–20%. Aleppo oak galls are used commercially. Old oaks have been found in peat bogs, which have iron present in the water, surrounded by an inky liquid formed without human intervention.

Iron gall ink was used in the Dead Sea Scrolls, to draft the US constitution, by Rembrandt and van Gogh to draw with and by J.S. Bach write down his compositions.[8] Although not widely used today, the use of permanent blue-black iron gall ink (Registrars' Ink) is a requirement in the UK for legal documents such as birth, marriage and death certificates, in ships' logbooks and in clergy rolls.

However, documents written with iron gall ink can be susceptible to ink corrosion which, in severe cases, can result in pieces of text being lost. The process causing this is not fully understood, but an important factor is the presence of excess iron(II) sulfate. Oxidation to iron(III) produces free radicals which attack organic molecules like cellulose in paper. Acidic conditions or high humidity make the problem worse.[9] However, when the ink is correctly formulated and the documents stored appropriately and carefully handled, little or no damage is observed even after hundreds of years.

The thick, outer bark of the cork oak (*Quercus suber*) was used by the Romans to make sandals and buoys.[10] Today it is used to make stoppers for wine bottles, in badminton shuttlecocks and sometimes in walls, doors and flooring, harnessing its insulating, fire-retardant properties. The word 'cell' was coined by Robert Hooke in the 1660s to describe what living things consist of. He was looking at a piece of cork under a microscope; the series of walled boxes he saw reminded him of the tiny rooms (or *cellula*) occupied by monks.

Legend attributes the use of cork stoppers for wine bottles to the French monk Dom Pérignon. The resulting extended storage time gave the wine industry a huge economic boost. The cork contains a waxy substance called suberin which acts as a barrier to water. Suberin is a complex biopolyester made up of fatty acids and aromatic compounds linked together into a three-dimensional network. Its potential uses include to firm human skin and reduce wrinkles and to prevent some types of cancer, as well as in the production of new polymeric materials.[11]

Cork oak is native to southwestern Europe and northern Africa, often growing in locations where there are hot, dry summers and cold, moist winters. The bark, which can be up to 30 cm thick, offers the tree protection from heat and cold, as well as from forest fires. Buds, buried deep under the bark, epicormically resprout even after a high-intensity fire (*i.e.* regrowth occurs from above-ground structures), allowing the tree to regenerate.[12]

Sections of bark are harvested from a living tree so the process must be carefully managed. Bark can be harvested every 10 years or so and, while the cork replenishes, the primary value of the trees is as a source of acorns to feed pigs. It was estimated that Portugal's cork oak woods absorb carbon dioxide equivalent to that produced by 185,000 cars a year. If the popularity of cork declines (*e.g.* by the replacement of corks by screw-caps or plastic caps) their potential loss would

Acorns

Cork oak (*Quercus suber*)

increase global warming. Although the production of corks does produce some greenhouse gases, the use of aluminium closures produces 25 times more and plastic caps produce 10 times more.[13]

## References:

1. www.chelsea-pensioners.co.uk/foundersday [Accessed 28.10.16]

2. www.bradgatepark.org/about-us-2/history-of-the-park/ [Accessed 28.10.16]

3. http://www.experiencenottinghamshire.com/discover/major-oak-p586841 [Accessed 28.10.16]

4. BBC News, (14th November 2014); 'Robin Hood' Major Oak wins Tree of the Year competition; http://www.bbc.co.uk/news/uk-england-nottinghamshire-30052751 [Accessed 28.10.16]

5. BBC News, (1st October 2002); Illegal acorns for sale on net; http://news.bbc.co.uk/1/hi/england/2289959.stm [Accessed 28.10.16]

6. J. Gunter, (16th May 2017); Don't put ground up wasp nest in your vagina; https://drjengunter.wordpress.com/2017/05/16/dont-put-ground-up-wasp-nest-in-your-vagina/ [Accessed 20.08.17]

7. C. Karnes, (1998); Make ink – Take half a pinte of water ...; The Iron Gall Ink Website; https://irongallink.org/igi_indexc69f.html [Accessed 30.10.16]

8. G. Farusi, (18th September 2007); Monastic ink: linking chemistry and history; *Science in School*, Issue 6; http://www.scienceinschool.org/2007/issue6/galls [Accessed 30.10.16]

9. G. Banik, (1998); Ink Corrosion – Chemistry; The Iron Gall Ink Website; https://irongallink.org/igi_index22a4.html [Accessed 30.10.16]

10. Plants of the World Online, Kew Science; *Quercus suber* L.; http://powo.science.kew.org/taxon/urn:lsid:ipni.org:names:296785-1 [Accessed 19.08.17]

11. J. Graça, (2015); Suberin: the biopolyester at the frontier of plants; *Front. Chem.*,3, 62; doi: 10.3389/fchem.2015.00062.

12. G.E. Burrows, L.K. Chisnall, (2016); Buds buried in bark: the reason why *Quercus suber* (cork oak) is an excellent post-fire epicormic resprouter; *Trees*, 30(1), 241–54; doi: 10.1007/s00468-015-1293-1

13. http://www.corklink.com/index.php/aluminium-and-plastic-closures-vs-cork-the-environmental-battle/ [Accessed 29.10.16]

**Autumn leaves**

# Beech

## (*Fagus sylvatica*)

Beech was considered to be a holy tree and prayers said under a beech were thought to go straight to heaven. Swearing under the tree reputedly caused it to rustle in protest and if offence was severe a branch might fall off. Dried leaves were sometimes used to fill mattresses but, although soft and fragrant, rustling of the leaves made sleeping on the mattress difficult. This earned beech mattresses the nickname '*lits de parlement*' or talking beds. The leaves were particularly used in mattresses or duvets for the bedridden to invoke the healing power of Nature for the patient. The leaves were also traditionally used in a poultice to relieve swelling.

Young leaves are lime-green and have silky hairs. The colour darkens as the leaves mature and hair is retained only at the leaves' wavy edges. Both male and female catkins grow on the same tree. Male catkins are tassel-like and hang from long stalks, while female flowers grow in pairs, surrounded by a cupule. After pollination, one or two nuts (also known as masts) form within. Once the cupules have been shed by the nuts they are sometimes used in dried flower arrangements.

Currently, the tallest native tree in the UK is a common or European beech (*Fagus sylvatica*), in Newtimber Woods on the Devil's Dyke Estate in West Sussex, standing 144 ft tall.[1] Beech bark is silver-grey and soft. It doesn't heal on cutting, making it a popular choice for those who want to carve their initials on a tree. However, the cambium layer, where the tree produces

**Beech** is the Bach flower remedy for those who are critical and intolerant of others.

new cells, is close to the surface of the trunk so beech trees are especially susceptible to injury and sensitive to light. Beech foliage is dense, stopping around 80% of sunlight reaching the ground and offering protection to the bark. Trees growing in the open tend to branch lower down on the trunk than those in forests where they benefit from the shade of other trees. The floor of a beech forest is cool and shady, favouring the growth of shade-loving plants. Beech can be used in hedging and if clipped doesn't shed its leaves.

The origin of the word book, from the Proto-Germanic *bokiz* (for beech), may be related to the practice of carving on beech trees. An alternative suggestion is that ancient runes were inscribed on beech tablets. Other uses of the wood include to make furniture, coat-hangers, wooden spoons and rolling pins. It was traditionally burned to smoke herring and meats. Beech tar was used for its antiseptic properties to treat psoriasis, eczema and other skin conditions. It was also an ingredient of an expectorant used for bronchitis.

The US lager Budweiser is aged over beech wood chips for 21 days.[2] However, as these are boiled with bicarbonate of soda before use they have little or no effect on the taste. The use of beech wood chips is said to aid the fermentation process and give a smoother lager. The chips may hold more yeast in contact with the beer, encourage yeast to settle and reduce the amount of dead yeast present.[3]

Beech wood can be burned to produce soot which is then diluted and boiled with water to produce the dark grey-brown pigment bistre. Other woods such as oak can also be used and the precise colour of the pigment depends on the wood involved. Bistre, sometimes known as soot brown, was used by some of the Old Masters including Rembrandt, Claude Lorrain and Thomas Gainsborough. The pigment is transparent so was applied to pen and ink drawings to evoke shadows.[4]

Beech nuts are edible, although their high tannin content makes them mildly toxic in large quantities. The trees contain potash, mainly potassium carbonate, which can cause feelings of giddiness and headaches if too many nuts are consumed. The genus name, *Fagus*, comes from a Greek word meaning to eat, referring to the edible nature of the nuts. In France nuts are sometimes roasted and used as a coffee substitute. They contain around 20% of a non-drying oil which can be extracted and used for cooking.

The Beech-Nut food company traces its origins to 1890 when, as The Imperial Packing Company, it

A portion of cellulose

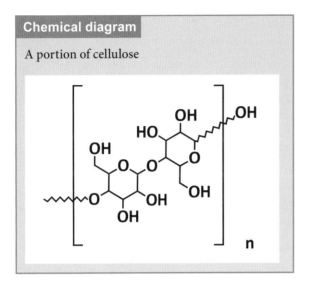

**Empty cupules**

**Male catkins**

began selling ham which was smoked in barrels to a traditional recipe. In the UK, the company was best known for its Beech-Nut chewing gum, available from 1910.[5] Now solely a baby-food company, Beech-Nut was involved in a scandal in the 1980s when its apple juice was found to be nothing more than water with sugar and flavourings. The apple concentrates from which the juice was made were adulterated and Beech-Nut repeatedly ignored quality warnings. In 1987, the company pleaded guilty to mislabelling the product with the intention to mislead and defraud the public and paid a fine of $2,000,000.[6] The next year, former chief executive Niels Hoyvald and former vice president John Lavery were each sentenced to a year and a day in prison and fined $100,000.[7]

Cellulose is a polysaccharide (a polymeric molecule made from glucose units) found in plant cell walls and fibres. Cellulose from beech wood pulp is processed to form modal, a soft fibre often blended with cotton, wool or synthetic fibres and used in clothing and household furnishings. The process involves steps to chemically alter then regenerate the cellulose to purify it and modify its properties. Pulp is first treated with sodium hydroxide to produce alkali cellulose. This is reacted with carbon disulfide ($CS_2$) to form cellulose xanthate, in which the hydrogen atoms of hydroxy (OH) groups in cellulose are replaced by $CS_2$. The xanthate is dissolved in dilute sodium hydroxide solution, filtered, deaerated, ripened and passed through spinnerets into a sulfate regenerating bath.[8] A spinneret, named after the silk-producing organ of spiders or other silk-producers, is a metal plate with holes which the solution is forced through to produce continuous fibres.

Next, the fibres are stretched, cut, desulfurised and bleached with a sodium hypochlorite solution or a hydrogen peroxide solution. They are repeatedly washed between the individual treatment steps. After the last wash, finishing agents are applied to ensure the desired running and gliding properties required for further processing. Although the raw material comes from a natural source, because of its extensive processing modal is considered a semi-synthetic fibre.

Modal is termed a second-generation rayon, characterised by its high strength when wet. This means that, unlike traditional rayon, garments made from modal can be machine-washed and tumble dried without shrinkage. Another feature is modal's extra softness, making it ideal for use next to the skin. As the surface is smooth, mineral residues such as limescale in water are not deposited on the textiles so fabric hardening does not occur.[9] The process by which modal is made non-shrink was developed in Japan in 1951 by S. Tachikawa.[10]

The parasitic plant *Epifagus virginiana*, known as beechdrops, can often be found on the roots of the American beech (*Fagus grandifolia*). The plant is astringent and was traditionally used to treat bowel conditions and applied locally to wounds or ulcers to prevent gangrene. Although sometimes known

**Beechdrops (*Epifagus virginiana*)**

as cancer root, there is no scientific evidence for its effectiveness in the treatment of cancer. One of its chemical components is orobanchin, an anti-inflammatory and antimicrobial agent. Otherwise known as verbascoside, it is also found in vervain (*Verbena officinalis*, see vervain section for more details) and olive trees (*Olea europaea*). The plant is a true parasite, getting all its nutrients from the beech tree *via* an appendage called a haustorium which penetrates the tissue of the beech root. Beechdrops contain no chlorophyll and the stems are brown while the small flowers are white or purple.[11]

## References:

1. BBC News, (16th April 2015); Devil's Dyke beech crowned Britain's tallest native tree; http://www.bbc.co.uk/news/uk-england-sussex-32331809 [Accessed 29.01.17]

2. http://www.budweiser.com/en/our-brand/our-process.html [Accessed 29.01.17]

3. M. Oldenburg, (31st December 2015); https://www.quora.com/How-is-Budweiser-beechwood-aged [Accessed 29.01.17]

4. Encyclopaedia Britannica; https://www.britannica.com/art/bistre [Accessed 29.01.17]

5. http://www.fundinguniverse.com/company-histories/beech-nut-nutrition-corporation-history/ [Accessed 23.08.17]

6. L. Buder, (14th November 1987); Beech-Nut is fined $2 million for sale of fake apple juice; The New York Times; http://www.nytimes.com/1987/11/14/business/beech-nut-is-fined-2-million-for-sale-of-fake-apple-juice.html [Accessed 30.01.17]

7. L. Buder, (17th June 1988); Jail terms for 2 in Beech-Nut case; The New York Times; http://www.nytimes.com/1988/06/17/business/jail-terms-for-2-in-beech-nut-case.html [Accessed 30.01.17]

8. Lenzig.com; Fibers: Viscose and modal fiber production; http://www.lenzing.com/en/fibers/viscose-and-modal-fiber-production.html [Accessed 29.01.17]

9. E. Mass; Rayon, Modal, and Tencel - Environmental Friends or Foes; http://www.yesitsorganic.com/rayon-modal-tencel-environmental-friends-or-foes.html#axzz4X9cNDU5f [Accessed 29.01.17]

10. Museum of Fine Arts, Boston, CAMEO Materials Database; Modal Fiber; http://cameo.mfa.org/wiki/Modal_fiber [Accessed 29.01.17]

11. http://www.herbs2000.com/herbs/herbs_beechdrops.htm [Accessed 23.08.17]

# Holly

*(Ilex aquifolium)*

Holly is an evergreen shrub or small tree. The red berries are an important food source for birds during the winter, when repeated freezing and melting softens them and makes them taste milder. Mistle thrushes (*Turdus viscivorus*) have been known to vigorously guard the berries to prevent other birds from eating them. Berries are only produced by female plants. Flowers are small, tinged pink on the outside and white within. Female flowers are larger than male ones. They require bees for pollination and these are attracted by a scent like honey which the flowers release.

Traditionally, holly was believed to offer protection from witches and sorcery. Some farmers allowed holly to grow taller within a hedge to prevent witches running along it. Their reluctance to cut it back may also be connected to the idea that it was unlucky to cut holly except at Christmas. It was, however, acceptable to pull branches off in a method considered fit for a sacred tree. The shiny leaves reflect light and, in combination with the bright red berries, they were often brought into the house in winter to lift the spirits. Holly was sometimes called Christ's thorn, in the belief that it sprung up where Christ walked on earth. Pliny the Elder, the Roman official and writer, referred to holly as aquifolius, literally needle leaf.

In parts of Britain, prickly leaves were denoted he-holly and smooth leaves were she-holly. When leaves were brought into the home at Christmas, if he-holly entered first then the man would rule for

**Holly** is the Bach flower remedy for those feeling hatred, jealousy or envy.

the next year. She-holly leaves predicted the woman would be in charge for the forthcoming year! In Celtic mythology, the Holly King ruled from the summer solstice to the winter solstice, when he was replaced by the Oak King. The Holly King was depicted as a man covered in holly leaves and branches with a holly club. The changeover is still marked in some places around Twelfth Night in mummers' plays.

Birdlime is a natural glue used as an insecticide or to trap birds for food in parts of Europe, Africa and Asia. In Europe, it is made from holly bark which is stripped, boiled, fermented and pounded to produce the birdlime. To catch birds it is smeared on twigs and branches near a decoy bird or a recording of birdsong. The decoy's calls attract passing birds which get caught in the birdlime when they land. Struggling to get free, they often become more stuck and pull out some feathers.[1] Use of birdlime or other methods to indiscriminately trap birds is banned in many places, including the EU. However, the practice persists in parts of Spain, Greece, Malta and Cyprus. In Spain, an estimated 4 million wild birds a year are illegally trapped.[2]

Birdlime was used during the development of sticky bombs, anti-tank grenades developed by Britain during World War II. Although not used in the final design, the successful sticky material was devised by Kay Brothers of Stockport who also manufactured birdlime.[3] The grenade was made up of a glass sphere filled with nitroglycerine gel and covered with a stockinette of knitted wood fibre. This was coated in the sticky substance and encased in a metal cover in two halves. To use the grenade, the cover was ejected, the priming pin pulled and the sticky bomb thrown or attached to the target as a lever was pulled, activating the fuse. On hitting the target, the glass shattered and the explosive material spread out, increasing the surface area it came into contact with.[4]

The protective casing being clipped into place around the glass flask of a sticky bomb, 1943

There were, however, problems with using the grenades; to make sure the bomb reached its target, soldiers had to get relatively close. Also, the stickiness could be an issue and grenades might not stick if the target was wet or muddy. Sometimes they stuck to the wrong target *e.g.* the soldier or his equipment. This was parodied in an episode of the sitcom Dads' Army, The Fallen Idol, where Corporal Jones' attempt at using a sticky bomb leaves it stuck to a bin lid rather than the target. However, 2.5 million of the bombs were manufactured between 1940 and 1943 and they were used by the British, Canadian and Australian armies and French resistance, as well as by the British Home Guard. Primarily, they were used against armoured cars and light tanks.[4]

Holly wood is white, hard and dense and was sometimes dyed to resemble more expensive woods such as ebony. It was also used to make tool-handles and bobbins and in Tunbridge ware objects.[5] These were typically boxes made using a tessellated mosaic technique developed in Tonbridge and Tunbridge Wells in Kent. The popularity of Tunbridge ware reached its peak in the mid-19th century, appealing to tourists visiting the fashionable spa town of Royal Tunbridge Wells. Holly wood was also used to make white chess pieces. An association of holly with control manifested in the use of the wood to make whips for use by ploughmen and horse-drawn carriage drivers.[6] In Victorian times, the wood was used to make cloth spinning rods for looms as it was found to be less likely to snag cloth than other woods.

European settlers arriving in North America may have misidentified the native, unrelated toyon tree (*Heteromeles arbutifolia*) as holly. Popular belief suggests they named the area of Los Angeles where it was abundant Hollywood. However, another idea is that the name was suggested by Daeida, the wife of Harvey Henderson Wilcox, owner of 120 acres of apricot and fig groves near the Cahuenga Pass, in 1887, after she heard of an estate called Hollywood in Illinois and liked the name![7] Toyon is also known as Christmas berry or California holly and has red

berries and toothed leaves, making it a popular addition to Christmas decorations. However, reputedly, harvest of toyon for this purpose was banned in California in the 1900s (or 1920s in some versions of the story).[7]

Holly leaves are leathery and tough and stay on the tree for three or four years. As they take a long time to decay once fallen, leaf skeletons are often found beneath a holly bush or tree. Traditionally, holly was believed to protect against lightning. The edges of its leaves are thought to act as mini lightning conductors.[6] Although prickly leaves are a common characteristic of holly, not all leaves are prickly, even on the same tree. Leaves on branches closer to the ground are usually prickly and this growth may be related to herbivores browsing on them. Leaves on a given tree are found to be genetically identical, but their DNA has different levels of methylation (*i.e.* there are additional $CH_3$ groups on some of the bases making up the DNA) which may be a reaction to herbivore browsing. Methylation (or demethylation) can halt or promote expression of a given gene. In this case it triggers the growth of leaves with deterrent prickles.[8,9]

Medicinally, the leaves were used to treat jaundice, fevers, rheumatism, smallpox and as a diaphoretic (to induce sweating) and tranquiliser. Topically, leaves soaked in vinegar were used to cure corns and chilblains were thrashed with a holly branch. The juice of the leaves was used to stop a runny nose. The berries were used as a powerful emetic and herbalist Nicholas Culpeper recommended fresh berries as a purgative.

**Variegated cultivar**

However, he used dried, powdered berries to 'bind the body' and 'stop fluxes'. Holly (in this case *Ilex vomitoria*) was used in the 'Black Drink' of the Seminole people of North America. This was a purgative taken before the first grain of the growing season was consumed to ensure that it did not come into contact with any of the old grain.[10]

Holly contains compounds including ilicin (a bitter principle), ilexanthin, ilicic acid and theobromine. Ilexanthin, a phenolic compound also known as syringin, was first isolated from the bark of lilac (*Syringa vulgaris*). It contains a glucose group attached to a sinapyl alcohol and when taken orally, the glucose is released. Sinapyl alcohol has anti-inflammatory properties and is an antinociceptive (*i.e.* reduces sensitivity to pain).[11] Ilicic acid is

  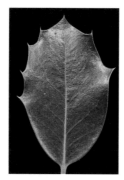  

**Variabilty in leaves on same tree**

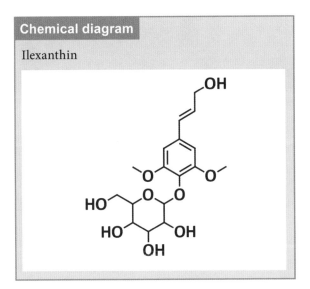
phytotoxic (*i.e.* it is toxic to plants) and may be present to deter competitors from growing nearby.[12]

The alkaloid theobromine is also found in cocoa, tea and cola and is used to treat asthma. It is toxic to dogs and cats in small quantities so renders chocolate poisonous to them. However, as cats can't taste sweetness, they are not attracted to chocolate[13] so chocolate poisoning of cats is virtually unknown. Theobromine is also toxic to humans but it is not present in large enough amounts in chocolate to be problematic. However, it is one of the compounds that makes holly berries toxic. It is estimated that a child can safely consume 1–2 berries but that 20 berries may be fatal.[14]

The dried leaves of another species of holly, *Ilex paraguariensis* or yerba mate, are used to make the drink known as mate, popular in parts of South America. This contains the stimulants theobromine, caffeine and theophylline, vitamins, minerals, antioxidants and amino acids. It has anti-inflammatory, antioxidant, cytotoxic, antidiabetic and cholesterol-lowering effects and has been linked to weight-loss. However, although promoted as a healthy drink, concerns have been raised that it can increase the incidence of some types of cancer. Two possible factors have been identified. Firstly, leaves are traditionally dried in a smoky environment. This produces polycyclic aromatic hydrocarbons which are known carcinogens. Many producers are now air-drying the leaves to address this. Secondly, if mate, or any other drink, is drunk at a high temperature, the lining of the oesophagus can be damaged with a possible corresponding increase in the likelihood of developing oesophageal cancer. Drinking mate at lower temperatures is now recommended.[15,16]

### References:

1. Bird Ecology Study Group, (3rd November 2007); Trapping birds with birdlime; http://www.besgroup.org/2007/11/03/trapping-birds-with-birdlime/ [Accessed 02.02.17]

2. G. Tremlett, (4th November 2011); Millions of birds migrating to Spain face painful deaths in glue-filled traps; The Guardian; https://www.theguardian.com/world/2011/nov/04/birds-migrating-spain-killed-hunters [Accessed 02.02.17]

3. Stockport Libraries, (15th October 2014); Sticky bombs, manufactured by Kay Brothers, Stockport; WW2 People's War; http://www.bbc.co.uk/history/ww2peopleswar/stories/12/a2159912.shtml [Accessed 02.02.17]

**Mate**

4. No 74 ST Grenade (Sticky Grenade); http://www.home-guard.org.uk/hg/gren74.html [Accessed 24.08.17]

5. D. Brick, (2010); http://www.tunbridgeware.org/p/about-us/index.pl?id=2189 [Accessed 03.02.17]

6. http://www.hollyhillorchards.com/HollyFolklore-Facts.html [Accessed 03.02.17]

7. L. Higgins, (18th December 2013); California Holly: How Hollywood Didn't Get Its Name; Natural History Museum Los Angeles County; https://www.nhm.org/nature/blog/california-holly-how-hollywood-didnt-get-its-name [Accessed 03.02.17]

8. C.U. Barcus, (21st December 2012); Hollies get Prickly for a Reason; National Geographic News; http://news.nationalgeographic.com/news/2012/121220-holly-leaves-prickly-plants-science/ [Accessed 03.02.17]

9. C.M. Herrera, P. Bazaga, (2013); Epigenetic correlates of plant phenotypic plasticity: DNA methylation differs between prickly and nonprickly leaves in heterophyllous *Ilex aquifolium* (Aquifoliaceae) trees; *Bot. J. Linn. Soc.*, 171(3), 441–52; doi: 10.1111/boj.12007

10. http://www.thepoisongarden.co.uk/atoz/ilex_aquifolium.htm [Accessed 04.02.17]

11. J. Choi, K.-M. Shin, H.-J. Park, H.-J. Jung, H.J. Kim, Y.S. Lee, J.-H. Rew, K.-T. Lee, (2004); Anti-Inflammatory and Antinociceptive Effects of Sinapyl Alcohol and its Glucoside Syringin; *Planta Med.*, 70(11), 1027–32; doi: 10.1055/s-2004-832642

12. B.E. Abu Irmaileh, A.M.F. Al-Aboudi, M.H. Abu Zarga, F. Awwadi, S.F. Haddad, (2015); Selective phytotoxic activity of 2,3,11β,13-tetrahydroaromaticin and ilicic acid isolated from *Inula graveolens*; *Nat. Prod. Res.*, 29(10), 893-8; doi: 10.1080/14786419.2014.955489

13. D. Biello, (16th August 2007); Strange but True: Cats Cannot Taste Sweets; Scientific American; https://www.scientificamerican.com/article/strange-but-true-cats-cannot-taste-sweets/ [Accessed 04.02.17]

14. A.M. Helmenstine, (Updated 28th February 2017); https://www.thoughtco.com/poisonous-holiday-plants-609292 [Accessed 24.08.17]

15. http://guayaki.com/mate/130/What-is-Yerba-Mate%3F.html [Accessed 04.02.17]

16. C.I. Heck, E.G. De Mejia, (2007); Yerba Mate Tea *(Ilex paraguariensis)*: A Comprehensive Review on Chemistry, Health Implications, and Technological Considerations; *J. Food Sci.*, 72, R138–R151; doi: 10.1111/j.1750-3841.2007.00535.x

Blackbird (*Turdus merula*) eating holly berries

# Elm

*(Ulmus procera)*

English elm is a field elm cultivar, identified as *Ulmus minor* 'Atinia' (sometimes *Ulmus procera* or *Ulmus campestris*). Elm wood is tough and dense and does not become saturated with water. It has been used for floorboards, to make boats and furniture and, before cast-iron was widely available, for water pipes such as those used in the English towns of Liverpool and Hull. Coffins were also commonly made of elm wood and the tree was associated with melancholy and death. The tough inner bark was used to make rope and mats.

In Italy, elms were grown in vineyards to shade and protect the vines and to give them a structure to climb on. Although the trees produce a large amount of seeds, these are often infertile and elm typically reproduces *via* shoots and saplings which grow from the roots of old trees. Due to this vegetative reproduction, all the English elms growing in the UK are genetically identical – clones of a tree brought by the Romans perhaps to train their vines on and said to be Columella's 'Atinian elm'.[1] Columella was a Roman agricultural writer who introduced the Italian Atinian elm into Spain to use in his vineyards.

Elm trees are susceptible to attack from a fungus borne by elm bark beetles and the lack of genetic variation in English elm has had catastrophic effects. Dutch elm disease was first identified by Dutch scientists in 1921, following an outbreak which started around 1910. This was attributed to the fungus *Ophiostoma ulmi*. By the 1940s, the outbreak had died down having

**Elm** is the Bach flower remedy for those who feel temporarily overwhelmed by responsibility.

killed between 10 and 40% of elms in affected countries. Unfortunately, a more virulent strain caused by
*Ophiostoma novo-ulmi* soon arrived in Europe and
reached the UK in the late 1960s. Within a decade
an estimated 20 million trees, two-thirds of the
population, had died and since then at least another
5 million have succumbed. Spores of the fungus are
transferred by elm bark beetles of the genus *Scotylus*
(*Scolytus multistriatus*, the European elm bark beetle,
or the larger *Scotylus scotylus*).[2]

When a tree is infected it forms plugs in its xylem to
stop the fungus spreading, but this also stops water
and nutrients reaching the upper branches, so the
effects of infection are seen first in the crown and the
tree eventually dies. Traditional plant breeding techniques, such as hybridising with more resistant varieties, have had limited success and hybrids which are
more disease-resistant are now available. However,
the disease is still prevalent in existing trees. Careful
management, including felling of diseased trees, has
preserved some mature elm trees in areas such as
Brighton.[3] Elm has also survived in hedgerows where
the roots have put down suckers which can grow to
about 5 metres high before being attacked by the
fungus.

A range of chemical and biological treatments have
been tried to prevent or fight infection or deter or kill
the vector beetles. Antifungal agents such as stabilised allicin, obtained from garlic, can be injected
into the tree but these have not been widely used.[4] In
2001, scientists at Abertay University, produced elm
trees genetically modified with an antifungal gene.[5,6]
As under British conditions the tree only spreads
by suckers rather than seeds, the potential spread of
genetically modified (GM) elms is limited, but resistance from the public to the use of GM organisms and
a lack of successful field trials have so far prevented
release of the GM elms.

Insecticides such as DDT (dichlorodiphenyltrichlo-
roethane) were used in the USA to kill the vector
beetles but DDT was found to have an adverse effect
on wildlife[7] and human health. It is now banned

Avenue of English elms in Fitzroy Gardens, Melbourne

Beetle galleries created by feeding on a wych elm

*Ulmus glabra*

worldwide for agricultural use although its limited use is permitted in some places to kill mosquitos which carry malaria. Another possible chemical defence is provided by harnessing the beetles' pheromones. The fungus is carried by male beetles and these are attracted by compounds including α-multistriatin which are released by virgin female beetles when they have found a food source (*i.e.* an elm tree). Potentially, male beetles can be attracted away from the trees using α-multistriatin and trapped. Other pheromones involved are α-cubebene and 4-methyl-3-heptanol.[8]

Biological control has also been trialled in the UK. Trees are injected with a 'vaccine' of a strain of *Verticillium* fungus which triggers the tree's natural

defences and so makes it better prepared to resist subsequent infections.[9,10]

While English elms are seriously affected by the disease, wych or Scots elms (*Ulmus glabra*) and European white elms (*Ulmus laevis*) are much less so. Although both are susceptible to the fungus itself, they seem considerably less attractive to the elm bark beetles that carry the spores. This may be due to the presence of different chemical compounds, including the triterpene alnulin, in their bark.[11] Alnulin, also known as taraxerol, is found in many medicinal plants including the roots of dandelion (*Taraxacum officinale*). Among its medicinal effects are anticancer, anti-inflammatory and antimicrobial properties.[12]

Wych elm is a native tree in Britain, typically smaller than the English elm. Leaves share the English elm's characteristic unsymmetrical shape, but are larger (typically 7–16 cm compared with 4–9 cm for English elm). The name wych may come from the Old English for supple or twistable.

**Chemical diagram**

α-Multistriatin

A woman's body was found in a hollow wych elm in 1943. Believed to have been there for 18 months, the remains were found by four boys playing in Hagley Woods in Worcestershire. Initially, a ritual murder by gypsies was suspected, after a severed hand was found buried nearby, but in 1953 another story emerged. Was the victim, popularly nicknamed Bella, involved in a German spy ring? Two suggestions came to light – could she be Clarabella Dronkers, a Dutchwoman who had 'known too much' about the ring, or a German woman Clara Bauerle, recruited by the Nazis and, perhaps, parachuted into Britain around 1941? The case remains unsolved but since 1943 related graffiti including "Who put Bella in the witch elm" have regularly appeared.[13]

Elm inner bark was traditionally used to treat skin conditions and rheumatism. Ulmin, a black gum from the bark, was used as an astringent and to treat ringworm. A decoction of root bark was applied in a warm compress to soften hard tumours. Bark or leaves soaked in vinegar were sometimes taken as a treatment for leprosy and a decoction of leaves was said to help mend broken bones. Bruised leaves were packed around wounds and bound with bark to aid the healing process.

The inner bark of the related slippery elm (*Ulmus rubra*), native to North America, is rich in mucilage and is used in herbal medicine to treat inflammation of the mucous membranes, particularly in the digestive system. It can also be taken as a food during convalescence as it is nutritive and easily assimilated. Externally, it is sometimes applied in a poultice to treat boils, abscesses and ulcers. As the tree has no other commercial value, bark is stripped from the whole tree, usually causing it to die.

## Chemical diagram

Alnulin

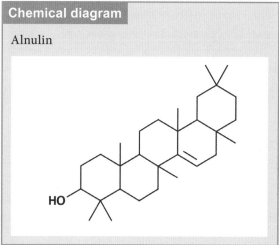

**References:**

1. L. Gil, P. Fuentes-Utrilla, Á. Soto, M.T. Cervera, C. Collada, (2004); Phylogeography: English elm is a 2,000-year-old Roman clone; *Nature*, 431(7012), 1053; doi: 10.1038/4311053a

2. C. Brasier, (1996); New Horizons in Dutch Elm Disease Control; Report on Forestry Research, 20–8; http://www.forestry.gov.uk/pdf/New_horizons_DED.

pdf/$FILE/New_horizons_DED.pdf
[Accessed 03.02.17]

3. http://www.brightonelmtrees.com/ [Accessed 03.02.17]

4. E. Dal Maso, L. Montecchio; unpublished results
quoted in https://www.trees.org.uk/Trees.org.uk/
files/45/4587f952-2baa-418f-bb8c-67471f7ba28d.pdf
[Accessed 04.02.17]

5. BBC News, (27th August 2001); GM trees fight Dutch elm
disease; http://news.bbc.co.uk/1/hi/scotland/1512210.stm
[Accessed 04.02.17]

6. K.M.A. Gartland, A.T. McHugh, R.M. Crow, A. Garg,
J.S. Gartland, (2005); 2004 SIVB Congress Symposium
Proceeding: Biotechnological progress in dealing with
Dutch elm disease; In Vitro Cell. Dev. Biol.–Plant, 41(4),
364–7; doi: 10.1079/IVP2005646

7. A.H. Benton, (1951); Effects on Wildlife of DDT Used
for Control of Dutch Elm Disease; J. Wildl. Manag.,
15(1), 20–7; doi: 10.2307/3796765

8. M.M. Blight, F.A. Mellon, L.J. Wadhams, M.J. Wenham,
(1977); Volatiles associated with Scotylus scotylus beetles;
Experientia, 33(7), 845–7; doi: 10.1007/BF01951234

9. http://dutchtrig.com/ [Accessed 04.02.17]

10. J. Postma, H. Goossen-van de Geijn, (2016); Twenty-four
years of DutchTrig® application to control Dutch elm
disease; BioControl, 61(3), 305–12;
doi: 10.1007/s10526-016-9731-6

11. D. Martín-Benito, M.C. García-Vallejo, J.A. Pajares,
D. López, (2005); Triterpenes in elms in Spain;
Can. J. For. Res., 35(1), 199–205; doi: 10.1139/X04-158

12. K. Sharma, R. Zafar, (2015); Occurrence of taraxerol and
taraxasterol in medicinal plants; Pharmacogn. Rev., 9(17),
19–23; doi: 10.4103/0973-7847.156317

13. Strangeremains, (24th April 2015); Who put Bella down
the Wych Elm?; https://strangeremains.com/2015/04/24/
who-put-bella-down-the-wych-elm/
[Accessed 04.02.17]

Elm wood

*Ulmus glabra* 'Camperdownii'

# Heather

## (*Calluna vulgaris*)

Common heather, or ling, was used as fencing, thatch, bedding, fuel and to make rope, baskets and brooms. Nails and pegs were fashioned from its roots and it was used as feed and bedding for livestock. The genus name *Calluna* comes from the Greek *kalluna*, to cleanse, and this may either be related to heather's use in brooms or to its cleansing taste.[1] The name ling may derive from the Norse *lyng* or the Anglo-Saxon *lig*, meaning fire.[1] Cut and dried heather was, and still is, used for heating and cooking in some places. Ling is associated with Scotland and an old belief held that purple heather was stained with the blood of the Picts. It is perpetually in mourning and will never grow on the graves of the clansmen killed at the Battle of Culloden in 1746. In parts of the Scottish Borders, burning heather was thought to cause rain. The success of heather in Scotland was aided by land-management – after deforestation, sheep or cattle were grazed on the land, followed by burning to maintain moorland for grouse-shooting. This allowed heather to flourish as it has good regenerative powers after fire and its new shoots provided food for grouse and livestock.[1] Heather is also one of two national flowers of Norway.

The aerial parts were used as a tonic and to treat consumption (tuberculosis), coughs and heart complaints. Today, its diuretic and antiseptic properties are harnessed to treat urinary tract infections such as cystitis. It rids the body of excess uric acid, benefitting people with kidney stones or arthritic joints. Bathing in heather-infused water can ease

**Heather** is the Bach flower remedy for those whose self-centredness drives others away.

rheumatism. In the Scottish Highlands, an ointment is made from heather tops and in other parts of Europe a liniment is made for arthritis and rheumatism by soaking the tops in alcohol. Heather tops make a pleasant tea, which is mildly sedative and said to help depression, insomnia and nervous exhaustion.[1] An orange-yellow dye can be made from the flowers using alum as a mordant (fixative). White heather is a symbol of good luck and planting a ring of it around an apple tree was believed to make the tree unusually fruitful.

Heather honey, where the bees have collected nectar exclusively from heather, has a higher moisture content than other honey. Both manuka and heather honey are what's known as thixotropic substances, *i.e.* they are a gel until stirred when they become a liquid. Recently, scientists at Glasgow University have demonstrated that Scottish heather honey is at least as effective as manuka honey as an antibacterial wound dressing for horses.[2] Manuka honey is currently the

only medical-grade honey available and it is used in veterinary medicine as a wound dressing. However, it can be expensive to import from New Zealand and using locally-sourced honey could provide a more cost-effective solution. However, of the 29 honey samples tested in the study, only 11 were free from bacteria, so honey must be carefully checked for contamination before use.[3]

Heather honey also has a distinctive colour, smell and taste making it prized alone or as an ingredient in foods and drinks. It is one of the ingredients of Atholl Brose and Drambuie whisky-based liqueurs and in cranachan, a traditional Scottish dessert also containing oats, cream, whisky and raspberries.[4] Characteristic chemical markers of honey from *Calluna vulgaris* are phenylacetic acid, a plant auxin responsible for the honey aroma, dehydrovomifoliol and 4-(3-oxo-1-butynyl)-3,5,5-trimethylcyclohex-2-en-1-one.[5]

Chlorogenic acid

Chlorogenic acid lowers blood pressure,[11] has anti-inflammatory effects and can protect against some age-related degenerative diseases.[12] It affects the metabolism of sugar and it may help prevent and treat type 2 diabetes.[13,14] The amount of chlorogenic acid in food plants such as tomatoes can be increased by genetic engineering to potentially benefit human health. This has been achieved by eliciting over-expression of the gene which produces chlorogenic acid naturally in the plant. The plants produce tomatoes with higher antioxidant activity and bacterial resistance that could act as functional foods.[15] However, chlorogenic acid has also been suggested to promote the laxative action of prunes![16]

Heather ale has been made in Scotland since at least 2000 BCE. Evidence of a fermented drink made with heather was found on a Neolithic pottery shard on the island of Rum. It is made by boiling the flowering tops of the plants and myrtle leaves with malted barley. The heather and myrtle provide bittering and flavouring agents. Brewing using any ingredients other than hops and malt was banned after the Act of Union of the Scottish and English parliaments in 1707, but hops can't be grown in Scotland and illicit brewing of heather ale continued. In 1992 commercial production resumed using a traditional recipe.[6]

Another modern use for heather stems is in the making of jewellery by Heathergems, in Pitlochry, Perthshire. The stems are hand-picked then blasted to remove the bark and foliage. The clean wood is vacuum-dyed then soaked in epoxy resin, cured and compressed into blocks which can be sliced. From each slice, shaped pieces are cut and are lacquered, polished and mounted to form necklaces, rings, bracelets and other items.[7]

The shoots of heather contain chlorogenic acid and its 3-O-glucoside, 3-O-galactoside and 3-O-arabinoside derivatives (where a glucose, galactose or arabinose sugar molecule is attached to the chlorogenic acid molecule).[8] Chlorogenic acid is found in many plants and acts as an antioxidant in both plants and animals.[9] It is abundant in green coffee extract which is marketed as a food supplement claimed to help with weight loss. There is some evidence to suggest it is effective for this purpose.[10]

Heather is usually considered to be a low value plant material, growing abundantly in heathland and moorland. However, it could offer a new business opportunity to farmers as a source for valuable triterpenoids such as α-amyrin, β-amyrin, uvaol, taraxasterol, lupeol, ursolic acid and oleanolic acid which are obtained from the surface waxes of the aerial parts.[17] It may be possible to use a benign extraction and fractionation method developed by scientists in York to extract these 'green' chemicals on an industrial scale.[18]

**Dyed bundles of heather stems**

**Heathergems jewellery**

## References:

1. Incredible Edible Todmorden; Herb of the Month Heather; https://www.incredible-edible-todmorden.co.uk/apothecary/herbofmonth [Accessed 06.02.17]

2. R. Carnwath, E.M. Graham, K. Reynolds, P.J. Pollock, (2014); The antimicrobial activity of honey against common equine wound bacterial isolates; *Vet. J.*, 199(1), 110–4; doi: 10.1016/j.tvjl.2013.07.003

3. Phys.org, (30th September 2013); Scottish heather honey is best for beating bacteria; https://phys.org/news/2013-09-scottish-heather-honey-bacteria.html [Accessed 06.02.17]

4. http://www.honeytraveler.com/single-flower-honey/heather-honey/ [Accessed 06.02.17]

5. C. Guyot, V. Scheirman, S. Collin, (1999); Floral origin markers of heather honeys: *Calluna vulgaris* and *Erica arborea*; *Food Chem.*, 64(1), 3–11; doi: 10.1016/S0308-8146(98)00122-8

6. Huntingtower; Did You Know? Fraoch Leann (Heather Ale); http://www.rampantscotland.com/know/blknow_heatherale.htm [Accessed 07.02.17]

7. https://www.heathergems.com/makingheathergems.php [Accessed 07.02.17]

8. M.A.F. Jalal, D.J. Read, E. Haslam, (1982); Phenolic composition and its seasonal variation in *Calluna vulgaris*; *Phytochem.*, 21(6), 1397–401; doi: 10.1016/0031-9422(82)80150-7

9. https://examine.com/supplements/chlorogenic-acid/ [Accessed 08.02.17]

10. I. Onakpoya, R. Terry, E. Ernst, (2011); The Use of Green Coffee Extract as a Weight Loss Supplement: A Systematic Review and Meta-Analysis of Randomised Clinical Trials; *Gastroenterol. Res. Pract.*, 2011, Article ID 382852, 6 pages; doi: 10.1155/2011/382852

11. T. Watanabe, Y. Arai, Y. Mitsui, T. Kusaura, W. Okawa, Y. Kajihara, I. Saito, (2006); The blood pressure-lowering effect and safety of chlorogenic acid from green coffee bean extract in essential hypertension; *Clin. Exp. Hypertens.*, 28(5), 439–49; doi: 10.1080/10641960600798655

12. W. Shen, R. Qi, J. Zhang, Z. Wang, H. Wang, C. Hu, Y. Zhao, M. Bie, Y. Wang, Y. Fu, M. Chen, D. Lu, (2012); Chlorogenic acid inhibits LPS-induced microglial activation and improves survival of dopaminergic neurons; *Brain Res. Bull.*, 88(5), 487–94; doi: 10.1016/j.brainresbull.2012.04.010

13. A.E. van Dijk, M.R. Olthof, J.C. Meeuse, E. Seebus, R.J. Heine, R.M. van Dam, (2009); Acute Effects of Decaffeinated Coffee and the Major Coffee Components Chlorogenic Acid and Trigonelline on Glucose Tolerance; *Diabetes Care*, 32(6), 1023–5; doi: 10.2337/dc09-0207

14. S. Meng, J. Cao, Q. Feng, J. Peng, Y. Hu, (2013); Roles of Chlorogenic Acid on Regulating Glucose and Lipids Metabolism: A Review; *Evid. Based Complement. Alternat. Med.*, vol. 2013, Article ID 801457, 11 pages; doi: 10.1155/2013/801457

15. R. Niggeweg, A.J. Michael, C. Martin, (2004); Engineering plants with increased levels of the antioxidant chlorogenic acid; *Nat. Biotechnol.*, 22(6), 746–54; doi: 10.1038/nbt966

16. M. Stacewicz-Sapuntzakis, P.E. Bowen, E.A. Hussain, B.I. Damayanti-Wood, N.R. Farnsworth, (2001); Chemical Composition and Potential Health Effects of Prunes: A Functional Food?; *Crit. Rev. Food Sci. Nutr.*, 41(4), 251–86; doi: 10.1080/20014091091814

17. A. Szakiel, B. Niżyński, C. Pączkowski, (2013); Triterpenoid profile of flower and leaf cuticular waxes of heather *Calluna vulgaris*; *Nat. Prod. Res.*, 27(15), 1404–7; doi: 10.1080/14786419.2012.742083

18. J. Zhao, (2011); The extraction of high value chemicals from heather (*Calluna vulgaris*) and bracken (*Pteridium aquilinum*); PhD Thesis, University of York; http://etheses.whiterose.ac.uk/2019/2/Final_Thesis_of_Jiewen_Zhao.pdf [Accessed 08.02.17]

**Wild Oat** is the Bach flower remedy to help those who are ambitious but unfulfilled to find their true direction in life.

# Wild Oat

## (*Bromus ramosus*)

*Bromus ramosus*, commonly known as hairy brome, is one of around 170 brome grasses in the genus. It is a bunchgrass and grows in distinct clumps, usually in shade. The stems are hairy, particularly towards the bottom of the main stem, and carry drooping leaves. The brome grasses are classified in a different genus but within the same subfamily (Pooideae) as the common oat (*Avena sativa*) and both their genus names are Latin words for oats. Other relations include wheat, barley and rye which are also part of the subfamily.

Brome grasses are susceptible to infection by endophytic fungi which live within the grass but do it little or no harm. The fungi do, however, produce chemical compounds to protect themselves and their hosts. One common example is peramine, an alkaloid which acts as a deterrent to insect feeding, found in *Bromus ramosus* infected with *Epichloë bromicola*.

The best-known example of an endophytic fungus is *Claviceps purpurea*, which often affects rye, producing ergot(s) (of rye). It can also affect other cereal plants including barley, wheat and the brome grasses. The word ergot is sometimes used to describe the fungus but it is also used to refer to the sclerotium of the fungus *i.e.* the food storage body from which the sexual stage of the lifecycle develops after over-wintering. Ergots replace grains of rye and produce toxic compounds known as ergot alkaloids.[2] These cause two types of illness if infected rye is eaten, one convulsive and the other, commonly known as St. Anthony's fire, gangrenous. Initially, gangrenous ergotism was known as holy fire; it was thought to be a punishment from God and is characterised by burning sensations in the limbs. This is caused by constriction of the veins, reducing blood flow to extremities and can lead to infections and loss of fingers, toes and sometimes limbs.

After an outbreak in France in 1039, a hospital was set up to treat victims and this was dedicated to St. Anthony (patron saint of lost things and of amputees). Due to favourable weather conditions in France (for the fungus) and the widespread consumption of rye in the diet, outbreaks of ergotism were common. Monks eventually started an order of St. Anthony and established over 370 special hospitals which were symbolically painted red.[2]

Convulsive ergotism has been suggested as an explanation for the strange behaviour of the young girls who accused neighbours of witchcraft during the Salem witch trials of 1692.[3,4] However, this idea has been disputed.[5] Sufferers from convulsive ergotism experience hallucinations, delusions, spasms and shaking. Ergot was traditionally used to induce childbirth. Some ergot alkaloids with medicinal uses include ergotamine, which can treat headaches including migraines and ergonovine, used to control postprandial haemorrhage and cause uterine contractions.[2]

Now the cause of ergotism is understood as being ergot-contaminated grains, cases are uncommon.

**Ergot infected grain**

However, there were outbreaks last century in Russia in 1926–7 when 10,000 people were affected; in England, also in 1927, with 200 cases and in France in 1951 when the outbreak, infecting over 200 people and leading to four deaths, was traced to contaminated bread. Today, ergots are removed from rye seeds and other grains by a flotation method. The rye is stirred in a solution of 30% potassium chloride. Ergots are buoyant and can be skimmed off the top. Fields growing rye are deeply ploughed and crop rotation is also employed, to minimise infection.[2]

## Chemical diagram

Peramine

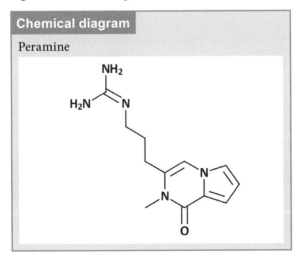

*Hordeum vulgare* (barley) with *Claviceps purpurea*

Study of the ergot alkaloids led their common nucleus to be identified as lysergic acid. In the 1930s, chemist Albert Hofmann was working on making derivatives of this acid and first synthesised the diethylamide which he called LSD-25. After taking some by accident in the 1940s, he tested it again on himself before riding home on his bicycle.[6] He described the hallucinatory properties of the compound, today known just as LSD, in detail. It went on to be used both legally and illegally for its hallucinogenic effects and its use is linked to counter-culture particularly during the psychedelic era (mid- to late-1960s). The day Hofmann first intentionally took LSD (19th April) is still commemorated as Bicycle Day.

The discovery and study of LSD and its effects on the brain made a significant contribution to the understanding of the link between neurochemistry and mental illness. Serotonin was found to have the same chemical framework as LSD and its connection to some mental illnesses was explored. Initially, LSD was taken to provide a model psychosis to allow psychiatrists to experience the world of the mentally ill. Today, many of the drugs used to treat mental illnesses act on serotonin neurotransmission, including Prozac (fluoxetine) and Zoloft (sertraline).[7]

LSD was tested in a CIA mind-control programme, Project MKUltra, a series of mostly illegal experiments carried out from 1953 and officially ended in 1973.[8] The drug was often given without consent including to prisoners, military and government employees and

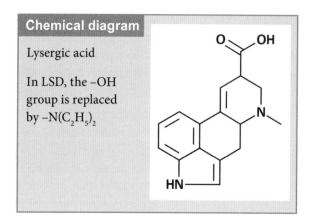

**Chemical diagram**

Lysergic acid

In LSD, the –OH group is replaced by $-N(C_2H_5)_2$

the public. The programme aimed to develop and test drugs and procedures for use in interrogations and torture, specifically by altering the victims' mental state. Use of LSD was eventually abandoned due to its unpredictable effects.

Throughout LSD's history of use and misuse, Hofmann maintained his belief that it is a valuable tool for psychoanalysis and psychotherapy and its vision-inducing powers provide a worthwhile tool of self-enlightenment. It was only the wrong and inappropriate use that led LSD to become his 'problem child'.[9]

Due to the close links between wild oat and commercially important food crops, it is sometimes used to test the viability of new techniques for soil or crop improvement. A series of experiments carried out in Tunisia monitored the growth of wild oat in soil treated with sediment from water storage reservoirs. While the use of treated municipal wastewater is beneficial for the management of water resources, it leads to a reduction in soil and crop quality. In addition, there is a build-up of sediment in the water storage tanks, reducing capacity. The experiments showed that the application of this sediment to the soil decreased the amount of metals, including zinc, copper and manganese, in the grain of *Bromus ramosus* probably due to these metals forming complexes with the sediment, so becoming immobilised. Use of sediment also increased the organic matter in the soil and improved its quality as well as neutralising the soil pH.[10]

Brome grasses have little economic value and are

**Psychedelic image**

Cheatgrass (*Bromus tectorum*)

Hairy brome (*Bromus ramosus*)

often considered to be weeds. The common names of *Bromus sterilis* are poverty brome or barren brome, attesting to this. *Bromus diandrus* is known as ripgut brome; this refers to the danger posed to animals by the seeds. These are sharp with backward-facing hairs which can become lodged like a fish hook. They easily work into the skin but are difficult to remove without causing damage.

The invasive weed cheatgrass (*Bromus tectorum*) is relatively fast-growing and regrows quickly after fire so interferes with the fire-cycle in natural plant communities. Plants grow closely together and die in early summer producing dense mats of combustible tinder. Therefore, cheatgrass increases the number of fires but is adapted to survive these events better than most other plants. The problem is worsened by increasing atmospheric carbon dioxide levels leading to an increase in the biomass of cheatgrass but a decrease in its attractiveness to herbivores (as it is less digestible) and in its decomposition. Stemming the spread of cheatgrass is a significant issue in parts of the USA due to the increased occurrence of wildfires.[11]

Researcher Ann Kennedy has shown that *Pseudomonas fluorescens*, a bacterium naturally present in soil, can inhibit the growth of the grass while leaving other plants unaffected. Cheatgrass's main advantage over other plants is that it has deep roots, which can stretch more than 30 inches into the ground. These grow earlier in the year and later into autumn than those of native plants, monopolising soil nutrients and water. The bacteria inhibit this root growth. However, while applying the bacteria would be preferable to using herbicides, it is expensive. Kennedy suggests a more viable method would be to use tanker aircraft to dump the bacteria on fire-breaks to clear them of any cheatgrass, so improving their action. One strain of the bacterium (ACK55) is expected to become available commercially in the near future.[12]

**References:**

1.  A. Leuchtmann, D. Schmidt, L.P. Bush, (2000); Different levels of protective alkaloids in grasses

with stroma-forming and seed-transmitted *Epichloë/ Neotyphodium* endophytes; *J. Chem. Ecol.*, 26(4), 1025–36; doi: 10.1023/A:1005489032025

2. http://www.botany.hawaii.edu/faculty/wong/BOT135/ LECT12.HTM [Accessed 18.02.17]

3. L.R. Caporael, (1976); Ergotism: The Satan Loosed in Salem?; *Science*, 192(4234), 21–6; doi: 10.1126/ science.769159

4. Secrets of the Dead, (2002); The Witches Curse; http://www.pbs.org/wnet/secrets/witches-curse/1498/ [Accessed 18.02.17]

5. A. Woolf, (2000); Witchcraft or Mycotoxin? The Salem Witch Trials; *J. Toxicol. Clin. Toxicol.*, 38(4), 457–60; doi: 10.1081/CLT-100100958

6. P. May, (1998); Lysergic Acid Diethylamide (LSD); http:// www.chm.bris.ac.uk/motm/lsd/lsd.htm [Accessed 18.02.17]

7. D. Nichols, (22nd December 2005); LSD: cultural revolution and medical advances; *Chemistry World*; http://www.rsc.org/chemistryworld/Issues/2006/January/ LSD.asp [Accessed 18.02.17]

8. Melissa – todayifoundout.com, (23rd September 2013); Project MkUltra: One of the Most Shocking CIA Programs of All Time; http://gizmodo.com/ project-mkultra-one-of-the-most-shocking-cia- programs-1370236359 [Accessed 19.02.17]

*Bromus ramosus* with ergot

9. A. Hofmann, ((c)1980); LSD – My Problem Child; McGraw-Hill Book Company, ISBN 0-07-029325-2; http://www.maps.org/images/pdf/books/ lsdmyproblemchild.pdf [Accessed 19.02.17]

10. S. Mtibaa, M. Irie, O. Hentati, H. Trabelsi, M. Kallel, M. Ksibi, H. Isoda, (2012); Soil Amendment by Sediment from Water Storage Reservoir as a Restoration Technique in Secondary Treated Wastewater Irrigated Area at El Hajeb Region (Sfax-Tunisia); *Journal of Arid Land Studies*, 22(1), 315–8; http://nodaiweb.university.jp/desert/pdf/ JALS-P71_315-318.pdf [Accessed 19.02.17]

11. L.H. Ziska, J.B. Reeves III, B. Blank, (2005); The impact of recent increases in atmospheric $CO_2$ on biomass production and vegetative retention of Cheatgrass (*Bromus tectorum*): implications for fire disturbance; *Glob. Change Biol.*, 11(8), 1325–32; doi: 10.1111/j.1365-2486.2005.00992.x

12. C. Solomon, (5th October 2015); Researcher Finds Way to Fight Cheatgrass, a Western Scourge; New York Times; http://www.nytimes.com/2015/10/06/science/ researcher-finds-way-to-fight-cheatgrass-a-western- scourge.html?_r=0 [Accessed 19.02.17]

Rye (*Secale cereale*)

# Gorse

*(Ulex europaeus)*

Also known as furze or whin, gorse often grows on waste ground and is sometimes considered to be a weed. Traditionally, it was used as fuel and produced ashes rich in alkali. These were used for washing, either as a solution or mixed with clay and made into balls as a substitute for soap, or as fertiliser. Gorse was also bruised or ground using a whin-stone and used as fodder. Pliny described using gorse in the collection of gold dust from water.

Although it burns readily, gorse quickly regrows afterwards from the roots. Gorse bushes can be found blooming in some places for most of the year leading to the saying,

> 'When Gorse is out of bloom
> Kissing's out of season'.

The sprig of gorse sometimes added to a bride's bouquet alluded to this. Gorse is not especially hardy and can be injured or killed by frost. The seed vessels burst in hot weather, scattering the seeds.

Medicinally, gorse flowers were used to treat jaundice and scarlet fever and the seeds included in medicines to treat 'the stone' (*i.e.* kidney stones *etc.*) and diarrhoea. Gorse was also used as an insecticide. An alkaloid with a powerful laxative effect was identified in the seeds and named ulexine. One use of ulexine was to treat cardiac dropsy. It was subsequently found to be identical to the compound cytisine found in broom (*Cytisus scoparius*)[1] and laburnum (*Laburnum anagyroides*).

**Gorse** is the Bach flower remedy for hopelessness and is sometimes described as 'sunshine in a bottle'.

Laburnum, the commercial source of cytisine

Cytisine is toxic, insecticidal and also acts as a partial nicotinic receptor agonist *i.e.* it partially blocks nicotine receptors and so can reduce cravings. Cytisine extracted from laburnum seeds is used in Eastern Europe to help smoking cessation. Elsewhere, a synthetic analogue called varenicline is used but this is more expensive and induces more side-effects than cytisine.[2] Comparing the relative cost of a standard course of treatment showed cytisine (25 days) cost $20–30, nicotine replacement therapy (8 to 10 weeks) cost $112–685 and varenicline (12 weeks) cost $474–501.[3] Since the monopoly on manufacture of cytisine was broken in 2012, a generic version has been on sale in Poland for $20 for a full course. The price and availability of this drug has been partially credited with the decline in smoking in Poland in recent years.[4]

However, this lack of monopoly is also problematic. Despite the existing data, including research studies

**Chemical diagram**

Cytisine

**Chemical diagram**

Varenicline

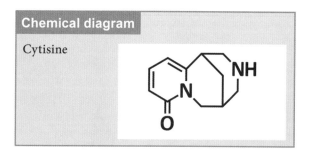

and information held on over 4,000,000 users, in order to become licensed worldwide more studies would have to be done. One reason preventing this is that cytisine is now out of patent which would limit the potential profit per treatment. However, the size of the market is large which could mitigate this. Other relevant factors may include previous investment in varenicline and financial interest in its continued use. Government funding of the required trial(s) is a possibility. The cost of a trial sufficient to permit licensing in the UK is estimated at £2,000,000 but a successful trial resulting in cytisine being used could save the NHS ten times this sum annually.[5]

Clinically, while there has been criticism of the weakness of the studies providing evidence to support use of cytisine,[6] the published data do suggest that it is at least as effective as varenicline and merits further consideration.[7]

Lectin I extracted from gorse is an anti-H agglutinin and can be used to identify people with the rare blood group h/h ($O_h$ or Bombay blood group).[8,9] This blood does not contain A and B antigens (so it appears to be of blood group O) but it does not express the H antigen, present in all other blood. This is important as individuals with Bombay blood cannot be given blood from any other group, as the presence of A, B or H antigens will stimulate an immune reaction. This

**Gorse with dingy skipper** (*Erynnis tages*)

causes the breakdown of red blood cells which are in circulation and can be fatal. Bombay blood was first identified in 1952 in India, where it is present in 1 in 10,000 individuals. This compares to 1 in 1,000,000 in Europe. It is more prevalent in closed communities where there is consanguinity (*i.e.* parents often have a common ancestor).

Lectins are found in plants, animals and micro-organisms and have a range of functions. They are proteins that bind to specific carbohydrates; the word lectin comes from the Latin *lectus*, meaning selected. The lectin known as UEA (*Ulex europaeus* agglutinin) is specific for the H antigen, so the absence of a reaction suggests the presence of Bombay blood. In this case, UEA is an antibody which causes H antigens in the blood to clump together (or agglutinate).

The best known plant lectin is ricin, found in the seeds of the castor oil plant (*Ricinus communis*). When castor oil is produced commercially, ricin is present in the waste. It is toxic to humans as it prevents proteins being produced in the body causing cells to die, but accidental exposure at a level likely to cause harm is unusual.[10] However, ricin can be extracted and purified and has been used as a terrorist or warfare agent. The 'umbrella murder' of Georgi Markov, a Bulgarian dissident, in London in 1978 was carried out by injecting a ricin pellet under his skin using a specially rigged umbrella. Ricin has been studied by both the US and the UK for potential warfare uses and it may also have been used by Iraq in the 1980s.[11]

More recently, letters were sent to former US President Barak Obama and New York Mayor Michael Bloomberg laced with ricin. Former actress Shannon Richardson was imprisoned for 18 years in 2014 after a plea deal in which she admitted sending the letters then trying to implicate her husband, who had filed for divorce.[12] Knowledge of the potential use of ricin increased after it featured in the US TV series 'Breaking Bad'. Two attempts to kill characters using ricin were shown. In the second one the character Lydia dies after ricin is added to her chamomile tea;[13] however, as ricin is inactivated at temperatures over 80°C, it is debatable whether this would work in reality! Ricin does have some beneficial effects; it can target and kill some types of cancer cells.[10]

Castor oil plant *(Ricinus communis)*

**References:**

1. S. Raja, K. Ravindranadh, (2014); *Cytisus scoparius*: A Review of Ethnomedical, Phytochemical and Pharmacological Information; *Indo Am. J. Pharm Res.*, 4(04), 2051–69; http://www.iajpr.com/archive/volume-4/april-2014/14april51.html [Accessed 23.02.17]

2. J. Leaviss, W. Sullivan, S. Ren, E. Everson-Hock, M. Stevenson, J.W. Stevens, M. Strong, A. Cantrell, (2014); What is the clinical effectiveness and cost effectiveness of cytisine compared with varenicline for smoking cessation: a systematic review and economic evaluation?; *Health Technol. Assess.*, 18(33); doi: 10.3310/hta18330

3. N. Walker, C. Howe, M. Glover, H. McRobbie, J. Barnes, V. Nosa, V. Parag, B. Bassett, C. Bullen, (2014); Cytisine versus Nicotine for Smoking Cessation; *N. Engl. J. Med.*, 371(25), 2353–62; doi: 10.1056/NEJMoa1407764

4. W. Zatoński, M. Zatoński, (2015); Cytisine versus Nicotine for Smoking Cessation; *N. Engl. J. Med.*, 372(11), 1072; doi: 10.1056/NEJMc1500342

5. P. Aveyard, R. West, (2013); Cytisine and the failure to market and regulate for human health; *Thorax*, 68(11), 989; doi: 10.1136/thoraxjnl-2013-203246

6. K. Cahill, N. Lindson-Hawley, K.H. Thomas, T.R. Fanshawe, T. Lancaster, (2016); Nicotine receptor partial agonists for smoking cessation; *Cochrane Database Syst. Rev.*, Issue 5, Art. No.: CD006103; doi: 10.1002/14651858.CD006103.pub7

7. P. Hajek, H. McRobbie, K. Myers, (2013); Efficacy of cytisine in helping smokers quit: systematic review and meta-analysis; *Thorax*, 68(11), 1037–42; doi: 10.1136/thoraxjnl-2012-203035

8. D.L. Bethesda, (2005); Blood Groups and Red Cell Antigens [Internet], Chapter 6 The Hh blood group; https://www.ncbi.nlm.nih.gov/books/NBK2268/ [Accessed 22.02.17]

9. N. Suraci, M. Mora, (2016); Bombay blood phenotype: Laboratory detection and transfusions recommendations; *Int. J. Blood Transfus. Immunohematol.*, 6, 8–11; http://www.ijbti.com/archive/2016-archive/100023IJBTINS2016-suraci/100023IJBTINS2016-suraci-full-text.php [Accessed 23.02.17]

10. Centers for Disease Control and Prevention, (updated 18th November 2015); Ricin toxin from *Ricinus communis* (castor beans); https://emergency.cdc.gov/agent/ricin/facts.asp [Accessed 23.02.17]

11. V.I. Roxas-Duncan, L.A. Smith, (2012); Ricin Perspective in Bioterrorism; *Bioterrorism*, Dr. Stephen Morse (Ed.), ISBN: 978-953-51-0205-2, InTech, Chapter 7, pp 133–58; doi: 10.5772/33392

12. CBS News, (16th July 2014); Texas woman in ricin case sentenced to 18 years in prison; http://www.cbsnews.com/news/texas-woman-in-ricin-case-sentenced-to-18-years-in-prison/ [Accessed 23.02.17]

13. http://breakingbad.wikia.com/wiki/Ricin [Accessed 08.09.17]

# Vervain

## (*Verbena officinalis*)

Vervain was believed to be a holy herb, used to staunch the wounds of Christ after crucifixion. Some of its common names are herb of grace, herb of the cross, *herba sacra* and holy wort. Vervain was used as an altar plant by the Romans and was also sacred to the Druids. In Holland, Germany, Finland, Slovakia and Denmark it is known as iron herb and was traditionally used in a procedure to harden steel and in love potions to promote love as hot as burning iron! Vervain by the doorstep was supposed to attract lovers and a sprig in a bridal bouquet, picked by the bride herself, would guarantee her husband's fidelity.

The name vervain may come from the Welsh *ferfaen* meaning to drive away stone and the plant was used to treat stones in the bladder. Another possibility is that it comes from *herba veneris* due to vervain's supposed aphrodisiac properties. The smell of the roots attracts pigeons, rats and cats and the plant was sometimes known as pigeon's grass.

Another common name for vervain is simpler's joy which may refer to its wide range of medicinal uses. A simple is a herbal remedy and simplers were those who foraged for medicinal herbs to sell to apothecaries. As vervain commonly grows near areas of human habitation, the name can be interpreted as referring to the simpler's happiness at knowing this valuable plant was close-by or their feelings when, on seeing the plant, they could anticipate shelter at the end of a long day![1]

Common vervain (*Verbena officinalis*) grows to about

**Vervain** is the Bach flower remedy for those whose over-enthusiasm may lead to burnout.

a mctrc tall and has lobed or toothed leaves. The white/mauve flowers are held on spikes. Other species in the genus include *Verbena hastata* (blue vervain), with deeper-coloured flowers and serrated leaves, which is common in the USA and *Verbena bonariensis* (purpletop vervain), native to South America, which has large, branched clusters of purple flowers and sparse, oblong leaves.

Around 30 complaints were treated using vervain. It was taken to improve sight, to treat fevers, plague and ulcers, for purging and to promote lactation. As a poultice, it was used for headaches, earache and rheumatism and also applied externally for piles. The poultice would colour the skin red and this was thought to be due to it drawing blood from the body. The herbalist Culpeper recommended use of vervain 'for those who are frantic'.

Vervain was also placed in fields to prevent bad weather. It was believed to handicap witches, protect against the evil eye and to have unique lock-opening properties. A man whose hand had been treated with vervain could turn keys and slide bolts at his slightest touch. In 1837, the British Pharmacopoeia recommended the wearing of vervain root tied with white satin ribbon as a necklace for protection from infection and evil influences.

Today, vervain is used in herbal medicine to treat stress, hysteria and nervous exhaustion. Also for depression related to chronic illness. A tea is sometimes taken for insomnia and two closely related compounds found in the extract, hastatoside and verbenalin, have proven sleep-promoting effects.[2] Verbenalin has one less –OH group than hastatoside and has potential liver-protecting effects[3] and anti-inflammatory activity.[4] Other beneficial compounds[5] include aucubin, which also has liver-protecting[6] and anti-inflammatory effects[4] and verbascoside.

Found in many plants, verbascoside has shown numerous biological effects including antibacterial, antifungal and anti-inflammatory actions. It is an antioxidant, protects the skin from damage from UV-light and has also shown anticancer activity.

*Verbena* sp.

## Chemical diagram

Hastatoside

traditional Chinese medicine, where it is known as *Ma Bian Cao* and taken to treat conditions including malaria, oedema and menstrual problems. Topically, it is recommended to treat wounds involving metal and for swollen sores and it is taken internally to kill parasites.[8]

The essential oil verbena, or lemon verbena, comes from the related plant *Aloysia citrodora* (sometimes *Lippia citriodora*, *Aloysia triphylla* or *Aloysia citriodora*). It is used in aromatherapy to help ease exhaustion, relieve anxiety, boost concentration and for its antibacterial, antiseptic and antispasmodic effects.[9] In perfumery and cookery, it offers a lemony fragrance and taste. It is one of the herbs used in the French liqueur *Verveine du Velay*.[10] Its citrus aroma makes it popular in herb gardens and to grow near windows and doors as the scent repels flies. Lemon verbena contains verbascoside but a study of the

Other potential benefits are in the treatment of neuro-degenerative diseases and pain. However, one potential problem is that verbascoside is quickly metabolised in the human body due to the multiple pathways in operation to eliminate plant-derived toxins. Further research is needed to enable its clinical use, but the compound may at least provide a basic structure for future development.[7]

Other uses of vervain in herbal medicine are as a hepatic remedy to treat inflammation of the gall-bladder and jaundice and as a mouthwash for gum disease and to prevent caries. The herb is collected before the flowers open and, considering its sacred nature, some people still cross and bless the plant with a commemorative verse when it is picked. It is used in

**Lemon verbena (*Aloysia citrodora*)**

antioxidant activity of the extract showed this was higher than predicted based on verbascoside content alone, suggesting possible synergistic effects.[11]

*Verbena* sp.

## References:

1. G. Evans, (2016); The Simpling Life; *Herbs*, 41(3), 16–7

2. Y. Makino, S. Kondo, Y. Nishimura, Y. Tsukamoto, Z.-L. Huang, Y. Urade, (2009); Hastatoside and verbenalin are sleep-promoting components in *Verbena officinalis*; *Sleep Biol. Rhythms*, 7(3), 211–7; doi: 10.1111/j.1479-8425.2009.00405.x

3. B. Singh, A. Saxena, B.K. Chandan, K.K. Anand, O.P. Suri, K.A. Suri, N.K. Satti, (1998); Hepatoprotective activity of verbenalin on experimental liver damage in rodents; *Fitoterapia*, 69(2), 135–40

4. M. del Carmen Recio, R.M. Giner, S. Máñez, J.L. Ríos, (1994); Structural Considerations on the Iridoids as Anti-Inflammatory Agents; *Planta Med.*, 60(3), 232–4; doi: 10.1055/s-2006-959465

5. Z. Liu, Z. Xu, H. Zhou, G. Cao, X.-D. Cong, Y. Zhang, B.-C. Cai, (2012); Simultaneous determination of four bioactive compounds in *Verbena officinalis* L. by using high-performance liquid chromatography; *Pharmacog. Mag.*, 8(30), 162–5; doi: 10.4103/0973-1296.96575

6. I-M. Chang, J.C. Ryu, Y.C. Park, H.S. Yun(Choi), K.H. Yang, (1983); Protective Activities of Aucubin Against Carbon Tetrachloride-Induced Liver Damage in Mice; *Drug Chem. Toxicol.*, 6(5), 443–53; doi: 10.3109/01480548309014166

7. K. Alipieva, L. Korkina, I.E. Orhan, M.I. Georgiev, (2014); Verbascoside — A review of its occurrence, (bio)synthesis and pharmacological significance; *Biotechnol. Adv.*, 32(6), 1065–76; doi: 10.1016/j.biotechadv.2014.07.001

8. http://www.americandragon.com/Individualherbsupdate/MaBianCao.html [Accessed 01.03.17]

9. Lemon Verbena Oil: The Oldie but Goodie Culinary Herb; http://articles.mercola.com/herbal-oils/lemon-verbena-oil.aspx [Accessed 11.09.17]

10. http://www.auvergne-tourism.com/articles/verveine-du-velay-emblem-of-auvergne-gastronomy-444-2.html [Accessed 11.09.17]

11. L. Funes, S. Fernández-Arroyo, O. Laporta, A. Pons, E. Roche, A. Segura-Carretero, A. Fernández-Gutiérrez, V. Micol, (2009); Correlation between plasma antioxidant capacity and verbascoside levels in rats after oral administration of lemon verbena extract; *Food Chem.*, 117(4), 589–98; doi: 10.1016/j.foodchem.2009.04.059

**Vervain leaves**

**Centaury** is the Bach flower remedy for those whose desire to please means they can't say no.

# Centaury

## (*Centaurium umbellatum*)

Centaury has a long history of medicinal and other uses. In the 18th century magical textbook, *Le Petit Albert*, it is listed as one of the 15 magical herbs of the Ancients and it is quoted by Breverton[1] as one of nine sacred herbs of the Anglo-Saxons (along with fennel, chervil, crab apple, nettle, betony, watercress, mugwort and plantain). If mixed with the blood of a female hoopoe bird and the mixture added to lamp oil and burned, it was said to cause all present to see themselves upside down with their feet in the air! An alternative description in *Le Petit Albert* states that mixing it with the blood of a female lapwing or black plover and burning made all others present appear to be witches. If burned at night when stars were visible, the stars would be seen to fight with each other.

Centaury was an ingredient in the remedy 'The Duke of Portland's Powder', said to have cured the Duke of gout. Named after the 2nd Duke, who popularised it, the powder contained birthwort, gentian, germander, ground-pine (a type of moss) and lesser centaury[2] (or just centaury).[3] The idea of using bitters to treat gout was not new and was suggested by Galen and others, but the Duke's patronage gave it credibility.

However, the doses taken were large and powder was advised to be used for two years. Although the treatment did cure the gout attack, patients were reported by Dr William Cadogan (a prominent physician and author of a 1764 book on gout) to die within six years, after suffering from apoplexy, asthma or dropsy. However, the English physician William Heberden, who gave his name to the Heberden's nodes which are a result of osteoarthritis, believed the powder had merit. Reported issues could be a result of the large dose which was indiscriminately given to all and some of the side-effects, such as apoplexy and paralysis, could be due to the condition itself. He stated that he had no doubt that the treatment was beneficial.[2] The powder eventually fell out of fashion and was replaced by other remedies.

The 2nd Duke of Portland (William Bentinck) (1709–62) never held public office and, apart from his publicising of the powder, is best known for a possible connection to the Great Bottle Hoax of 1749. A Duke, suggested to be Portland[4] or Montagu, wagered his friends that an audience would turn up in response to an advertisement saying an anonymous performer called the Bottle Conjuror would fit his body into a quart bottle. The audience duly turned up at the Haymarket Theatre in London but, when the performer didn't appear, they rioted. The dukedom lapsed in 1990 when there were no suitable heirs and reverted to an earldom. The current Earl of Portland is actor Tim Bentinck, best known for playing David Archer in the BBC radio series The Archers. He also provided the voice for 'mind the gap', used for 15 years on the London Underground Piccadilly Line.

Common or European centaury (*Centaurium umbellatum*) is more usually known as *Centaurium erythraea* and was previously called *Erythraea centaurium*.

*Erythraea* comes from the Greek *erythros*, for red, from the colour of the flowers (although these are often more pink than red). The genus was formerly assigned as *Chironia* after the centaur Chiron, famous in Greek mythology as a medical herbalist. Chiron reputedly cured himself using herbs after being accidently wounded by an arrow fired by Hercules, with a tip poisoned with the blood of the Hydra. The Hydra was a serpentine water monster whose breath and blood were poisonous. Centaury flowers grow in clusters on short stalks which spread from a common point, like the ribs of an umbrella. This arrangement is known as an umbel and indicated in the species name *umbellatum*.

In herbal medicine, centaury was used as a bitter tonic which acted as a gentle laxative and to treat heartburn. Its extreme bitterness was referred to in one common name, *Fel Terrae*, or gall of the earth, which was corrupted to felwort or filwort. Nicholas Culpeper, the 17th century herbalist, described it as 'very wholesome, but not very toothsome', suggesting is was useful but not pleasant to take. It was also used for its fever-reducing properties, reflected in one of its common names, feverwort, and to treat snakebites, sciatica, colic, jaundice, dropsy, cramp and many other conditions. As part of the gentian family, centaury shares a number of common names and uses with the gentians and also contains some of the same chemical compounds, including gentiopicrin (or gentiopicroside; see gentian section for more details). The aerial parts are still in use today to treat dyspepsia and as a digestive and gastric stimulant, indicated primarily for temporary appetite loss.

Centaury contains several bitter principles which contribute to its action on the digestive system including swertiamarin, gentiopicroside, centapicrin and sweroside (bitterness value 12,000), of which swertiamarin is the most abundant. Centapicrin is one of the most intensely bitter compounds known (with a bitterness value of 4,000,000) and is particularly abundant in the flowers.[5] Extracts of gentian are used in North African tribal medicine to treat diabetes mellitus and these show blood-glucose lowering effects attributed to a reduction in oxidative stress and pancreatic β-cell damage.[6] Swertiamarin has potential antidiabetic activity *via* its active metabolite gentianine.[7] Other possible benefits of centaury extracts include antipyretic (fever-reducing), anti-inflammatory[8] and liver-protecting properties.[9]

It can also act as a powerful antioxidant due to the presence of compounds with phenolic groups, such as ferulic acid, sinapic acid and *p*-coumaric acid which were all identified in a tea made from centaury.[10] Among the potential beneficial effects of centaury's antioxidant properties is the prevention of gastric ulcers.[11]

Ferulic acid is common in plants but it is often bound to cell walls or in insoluble fibres so has limited bioavailability. Studies of sweetcorn showed that cooking releases the ferulic acid, thereby increasing

### Chemical diagram

Centapicrin

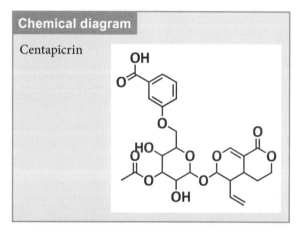

the beneficial properties of the corn (although cooking does reduce the amount of vitamin C). After 50 minutes of cooking at 115°C, the quantity of ferulic acid had increased by 900% and the total antioxidants by 53%.[12,13] Health benefits of ferulic acid are believed to be due to its antioxidant activity[14] and include anti-inflammatory, antidiabetic, anticancer and anti-ageing properties and protective effects for the liver, brain, lungs and against radiation. It is approved for use as a food additive in Japan. Ferulic acid can be used in the biotechnological production of vanillin, the flavour component of vanilla.[15]

### Chemical diagram

Ferulic acid

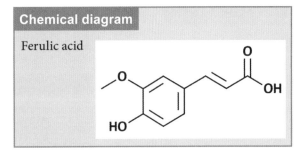

### References:

1. T. Breverton, (2011); Breverton's Complete Herbal; Quercus Publishing, London, ISBN 978-0-85738-336-5, p 87

2. A.B. Garrod, (1859); The Nature and Treatment of Gout and Rheumatic Gout, pp 447–50; https://archive.org/stream/naturetreatment00garr/naturetreatment00garr_djvu.txt [Accessed 02.03.17]

3. University of Nottingham; Recipe for gout powder sent by Henrietta Grey, Dowager Countess of Stamford to William Cavendish-Scott-Bentinck, 4th Duke of Portland; c. Aug. 1821 [Pw H 742]; https://www.nottingham.ac.uk/manuscriptsandspecialcollections/collectionsindepth/health/usedfor.aspx#history [Accessed 02.03.17]

4. W.S. Walsh, (1909); Handy-book of Literary Curiosities, J.B. Lippincott Co., pp 475–79; https://archive.org/stream/handybooklitera04walsgoog#page/n478/mode/2up [Accessed 02.03.17]

5. S.E. Edwards, I. da Costa Rocha, E.M. Williamson, M. Heinrich, (2015); Phytopharmacy: An Evidence-Based Guide to Herbal Medicinal Products, First Edition, John Wiley & Sons Ltd., ISBN 9781118543566, pp 88–90

6. M. Sefi, H. Fetoui, N. Lachkar, A. Tahraoui, B. Lyoussi, T. Boudawara, N. Zeghal, (2011); Centaurium erythrea (Gentianaceae) leaf extract alleviates streptozotocin-induced oxidative stress and β-cell damage in rat pancreas; J. Ethnopharmacol., 135(2), 243–50; doi: 10.1016/j.jep.2011.02.029

7. H. Vaidya, R.K. Goyal, S.K. Cheema, (2013); Anti-diabetic Activity of Swertiamarin is due to an Active Metabolite, Gentianine, that Upregulates PPAR-γ Gene Expression in 3T3-L1 cells; Phytother. Res., 27(4), 624–7; doi: 10.1002/ptr.4763

8. T. Berkan, L. Üstünes, F. Lermioglu, A. Özer, (1991); Antiinflammatory, Analgesic, and Antipyretic Effects of an Aqueous Extract of Erythraea centaurium; Planta Med., 57(1), 34–7; doi: 10.1055/s-2006-960011

9. M. Mroueh, Y. Saab, R. Rizkallah, (2004); Hepatoprotective activity of Centaurium erythraea on acetaminophen-induced hepatotoxicity in rats; Phytother. Res., 18(5), 431–3; doi: 10.1002/ptr.1498

10. P. Valentão, E. Fernandes, F. Carvalho, P.B. Andrade, R.M. Seabra, M.L. Bastos, (2001); Antioxidant Activity of Centaurium erythraea Infusion Evidenced by Its Superoxide Radical Scavenging and Xanthine Oxidase Inhibitory Activity; J. Agric. Food Chem., 49(7), 3476–9; doi: 10.1021/jf001145s

11. Y. Tuluce, H. Ozkol, I. Koyuncu, H. Ine, (2011); Gastroprotective effect of small centaury (Centaurium erythraea L) on aspirin-induced gastric damage in rats; Toxicol. Ind. Health, 27(8) 760–8; doi: 10.1177/0748233710397421

12. B. Friedlander, (8th August 2002); Cooking sweet corn boosts its ability to fight cancer and heart disease by freeing healthful compounds, Cornell scientists find; Cornell Chronicle; http://www.news.cornell.edu/stories/2002/08/cooking-sweet-corn-boosts-disease-fighting-nutrients [Accessed 03.03.17]

13. V. Dewanto, X. Wu, R.H. Liu, (2002); Processed Sweet Corn Has Higher Antioxidant Activity; J. Agric. Food Chem., 50(17), 4959–64; doi: 10.1021/jf0255937

14. M. Srinivasan, A.R. Sudheer, V.P. Menon, (2007); Ferulic Acid: Therapeutic Potential Through Its Antioxidant Property; J. Clin. Biochem. Nutr., 40(2), 92–100; doi: 10.3164/jcbn.40.92

15. T. Furuya, M. Miura, M. Kuroiwa, K. Kino, (2015); High-yield production of vanillin from ferulic acid by a coenzyme-independent decarboxylase/oxygenase two-stage process; N. Biotechnol., 32(3), 335–9; doi: 10.1016/j.nbt.2015.03.002

**Gentian** is the Bach flower remedy for those who are discouraged after a setback.

# Gentian

*(Gentiana amarella)*

Gentians are best known for their bitter roots and have been used in herbal medicine to improve digestion for over 3,000 years. Gentian root was an ingredient in the Duke of Portland's powder for gout, along with centaury (see centaury section for more details).[1] The genus name is a tribute to the Illyrian king Gentius who reigned between 181 and 168 BCE (when the Romans conquered the kingdom) and is reputed to have discovered the medicinal virtue of the plants.

Commonly known as bitterwort, autumn gentian, northern gentian or felwort (which is also a common name for centaury), species *amarella* is usually placed in the dwarf genus *Gentianella*. It grows to only about 30 cm high, producing pale violet flowers with four or five petals (sometimes a mixture of both on the same plant). Leaves occur in pairs and sometimes have a reddish tinge.

Gentian was one of several bitter herbs used in brewing before the introduction of hops. In the 18th century, gentian wine was drunk before dinner as an aperitif. Today, extract of the root is one of the main botanical ingredients of Angostura® aromatic bitters, a component of many cocktails.[2]

Used from 1824 by Dr Johann Siegert as a tincture to treat stomach ailments, the bitters were named after Angostura in Venezuela (today officially known as the Bolivarian Republic of Venezuela) where Siegert was stationed as Surgeon General to the armies of Simón Bolívar.[2] Bolívar liberated many South American countries from Spanish rule and the country of Bolivia is named in his honour.[3] In 1850, Siegert began exporting the bitters and soon afterwards they began to be used in cocktails. The business moved to Trinidad in 1875 and continued to flourish until 1906, when US laws were introduced limiting the alcohol content and preventing use of words like 'cure' on the label. Luckily, the bitters were now primarily used as a flavouring for food and drinks and this continues today.

The bitters do not make food and drink bitter but rather they act as antacids and enhance the other flavours present. Cocktails including a dash of Angostura bitters include Singapore Sling, Pink Gin and Manhattan.[2] Although the recipe for the bitters is secret, the gentian used is likely to be *Gentiana lutea* (yellow gentian).[4] Despite its name, the recipe doesn't include angostura bark extract, although this is an ingredient in another brand of bitters, Abbott's Aromatic Bitters.[5] Other drinks that include gentian root extracts include Campari, Aperol and the US soft drink Moxie.[6]

**Angostura aromatic bitters**

**Yellow gentian** *(Gentiana lutea)*

Herbalist Nicholas Culpeper reported that gentian 'comforts the heart and preserves it against faintings and swoonings'. As well as its use as a bitter tonic for the digestive system, gentian was also used to reduce fever, as an antiseptic, to expel parasitic worms and as an emmenagogue (so gentian should not be taken during pregnancy). Powdered dried root was used to treat bites from mad dogs and venomous beasts. During the Middle Ages, it was taken as an antidote to poison. Extracts of the roots of agueweed (*Gentiana quinquefolia*) were a treatment for intermittent fevers, used instead of quinine. A homoeopathic remedy made from agueweed can also be used for the treatment of fevers and stomach problems.

Extracts of *Gentiana lutea* are the most studied in the genus and these have a range of medicinal effects.[7,8,9] They inhibit aldose reductase (ALR2), an enzyme which converts glucose to sorbitol in cells. The accumulation of sorbitol has been implicated in some of the complications of diabetes including diabetic retinopathy and cataracts.[10] Antioxidant, antimicrobial, liver-protecting and anti-inflammatory

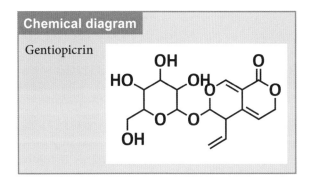

**Chemical diagram**

Gentiopicrin

properties of gentian have also been demonstrated.[7] In cosmetics, extracts are used to moisturise and protect the skin. An extract can be taken to treat sinusitis and is one of five components in the effective herbal drug Sinupret®.[11] Vervain extract is another of the ingredients.

The bitter principles in gentian include gentiin, gentiamarin, gentiopicrin and amarogentin.[12,13] Gentiopicrin, an anticonvulsant agent with potential antiaddiction and antianxiety properties, is also known as gentiopicroside.[14] It also has anti-inflammatory and antimicrobial activities, can reduce programmed cell death (apoptosis) and could potentially protect the liver against failure.[15] Amarogentin is one of the bitterest substances known (bitterness index value 58,000,000)[12] and is active against the tropical disease leishmaniasis, a parasitic infection spread by sandflies.[16]

Extracts of *Gentiana olivieri*, used in Turkish traditional medicine to treat diabetes, contain the flavone compound isoorientin which can lower blood glucose and lipid levels.[17]

The roots of autumn gentian contain gentisic acid. This is a minor breakdown product of aspirin in the human body and is excreted by the kidneys (see willow section for more information on aspirin). Gentisic acid is a strong antioxidant and this may be partly responsible for the antiatherogenic properties of aspirin *i.e.* it prevents the build-up of plaques on blood vessel walls.[18]

Gentian violet, a dye with antibacterial and antifungal properties which is used in the stain test to

detect Gram-positive bacteria, is not made from gentians. The name refers to the colour of the dye, which resembles that of blue-violet gentian petals. It is used to treat thrush and bacterial skin infections, to stain structures in the eye during surgery, to prevent transmission of Chagas disease in blood banks and also industrially in pen ink. The emergence of antibiotic-resistant bacteria and the low cost of gentian violet may lead to its more widespread use in future. In addition, it has shown antiparasitic, antiangiogenic (inhibiting growth of new blood vessels) and antitumour activities.[19]

## References:

1. University of Nottingham; Recipe for gout powder sent by Henrietta Grey, Dowager Countess of Stamford to William Cavendish-Scott-Bentinck, 4th Duke of Portland; c. Aug. 1821 [Pw H 742]; https://www.nottingham.ac.uk/manuscriptsandspecialcollections/collectionsindepth/health/usedfor.aspx#history [Accessed 02.03.17]

2. http://angosturabitters.com/ [Accessed 05.03.17]

3. http://www.who2.com/bio/simon-bolivar/ [Accessed 05.03.17]

4. A.O. Tucker, S. Belsinger, (2004); Bitters: Beverages with Moxie; http://www.motherearthliving.com/cooking-methods/bitters-beverages-with-moxie [Accessed 05.03.17]

5. http://abbottsbitters.com/about-abbotts-bitters [Accessed 05.03.17]

6. Gentian Research Network; Ethnobotany of gentians: Bitters, aperitifs, sodas, digestives and other drinkable (?) beverages; http://gentian.rutgers.edu/ethno_drink.htm [Accessed 06.03.17]

7. Y. Pan, Y.-L. Zhao, J. Zhang, W.-Y. Li, Y.-Z. Wang, (2016); Phytochemistry and Pharmacological Activities of the Genus *Gentiana* (Gentianaceae); *Chem. Biodiversity*, 13(2), 107–50; doi: 10.1002/cbdv.201500333

8. F. Mirzaee, A. Hosseini, H.B. Jouybari, A. Davoodi, M. Azadbakht, (2017); Medicinal, biological and phytochemical properties of Gentiana species; *J. Tradit. Complement. Med.*, 7(4), 400–8; doi: 10.1016/j.jtcme.2016.12.013

9. D.N. Olennikov, N.I. Kashchenko, N.K. Chirikova, L.P. Koryakina. L.N. Vladimirov, (2015); Bitter Gentian Teas: Nutritional and Phytochemical Profiles, Polysaccharide Characterisation and Bioactivity; *Molecules*, 20(11), 20014–30; doi: 10.3390/molecules201119674

10. C. Akileshwari, P. Muthenna, B. Nastasijević, G. Joksić, J.M. Petrash, G.B. Reddy, (2012); Inhibition of Aldose Reductase by *Gentiana lutea* Extracts; *Exp. Diabetes Res.*, vol. 2012, Article ID 147965, 8 pages; doi: 10.1155/2012/147965

11. D. Passali, J. Cambi, F.M. Passali, L.M. Bellussi, (2015); Phytoneering: a new way of therapy for rhinosinusitis; *Acta Otorhinolaryngol. Ital.*, 35(1), 1–8; PMCID: PMC4443571

12. A. Singh, (2008); Phytochemicals of Gentianae: A Review of Pharmacological Properties; *Int. J. Pharm. Sci. Nanotech.*, 1(1), 33–6; http://ijpsnonline.com/Issues/33.pdf [Accessed 05.03.17]

13. https://www.mdidea.com/products/new/new00603.html [Accessed 13.09.17]

14. S.-B. Liu, L. Ma, H.-J. Guo, B. Feng, Y.-Y. Guo, X.-Q. Li, W.-J Sun, L.-H. Zheng, M.-G. Zhao, (2012); Gentiopicroside Attenuates Morphine Rewarding Effect through Downregulation of GluN2B Receptors in Nucleus Accumbens; *CNS Neurosci. Ther.*, 18(8), 652–8; doi: 10.1111/j.1755-5949.2012.00338.x

15. L.-H. Lian, Y.-L. Wu, Y. Wan, X. Li, W.-X. Xie, J.-X. Nan, (2010); Anti-apoptotic activity of gentiopicroside in D-galactosamine/lipopolysaccharide-induced murine fulminant hepatic failure; *Chem. Biol. Interact.*, 188(1), 127–33; doi: 10.1016/j.cbi.2010.06.004

16. S. Medda, S. Mukhopadhyay, M.K. Basu, (1999); Evaluation of the in-vivo activity and toxicity of amarogentin, an antileishmanial agent, in both liposomal and niosomal forms; *J. Antimicrob. Chemother.*, 44(6), 791–4; doi: 10.1093/jac/44.6.791

17. E. Sezik, M. Aslan, E. Yesilada, S. Ito, (2005); Hypoglycaemic activity of *Gentiana olivieri* and isolation of the active constituent through bioassay-directed fractionation techniques; *Life Sci.*, 76(11), 1223–38; doi: 10.1016/j.lfs.2004.07.024

18. K. Ashidate, M. Kawamura, D. Mimura, H. Tohda, S. Miyazaki, T. Teramoto, Y. Yamamoto, Y. Hirata, (2005); Gentisic acid, an aspirin metabolite, inhibits oxidation of low-density lipoprotein and the formation of cholesterol ester hydroperoxides in human plasma; *Eur. J. Pharmacol.*, 513(3), 173–9; doi: 10.1016/j.ejphar.2005.03.012.

19. A.M. Maley, J.L. Arbiser, (2013); Gentian Violet: a 19th century drug re-emerges in the 21st century; *Exp. Dermatol.*, 22(12), 775–80; doi: 10.1111/exd.12257

# Agrimony

*(Agrimonia eupatoria)*

Common agrimony (*Agrimonia eupatoria*) is also known as church steeples, referring to its tall spikes of yellow flowers. Herbalist John Gerard stated it was useful for those with 'naughty livers', giving rise to the common name liverwort. Another name is philanthropos, from the Greek, which may refer to its beneficial properties. Alternatively, it might allude to the burs (seed vessels) that cling to the clothes of passers-by by the hooked ends of their stiff hairs, as if wanting to accompany them. This property is reflected in other common names including sticklewort. The toothed leaflets are hairy, as are the stems.

A decoction of the plant was used to treat gout and jaundice and as a purgative and tonic. Agrimony was used to staunch bleeding; in medieval times, it was primarily a battlefield herb. The plant features in preparations detailed in Anglo-Saxon medicinal texts from the 10th century for wound healing. A study showed it possessed antimicrobial activity against some common wound pathogens.[1]

Agrimony is one component of arquebuse water (arquebusade water), first mentioned in the 15th century and formerly used to treat wounds. The origin of the modern-day remedy can be traced to King Francis I of France who commissioned healing monks to develop a plant extract to treat damage from a heavy musket known as an arquebuse. The most effective of these was devised by the monks of Saint-Antoine monastery. Their water proved so effective in treating soldiers, not just with combat injuries but

**Agrimony** is the Bach flower remedy for those who hide their torment behind a cheerful face.

also with skin diseases and mouth infections, that its renown spread. From the monks' 1634 recipe, arquebuse water is made today in Switzerland and contains extracts of 75 plants. These include agrimony for its wound-healing properties, vervain with its astringent and wound-healing effects, centaury as an anti-inflammatory, dog rose, heather, oak and walnut. Called Arquebusade Herbal Water, it is used to treat many skin conditions including psoriasis and rosacea and to reduce wrinkles.[2] Agrimony was also an ingredient of some plague waters, popular treatments for plague in medieval Europe.[3]

The name agrimony may come from the Greek *argemone* which was sometimes used for plants which were healing to the eyes (particularly for treatment of cataracts); extracts are still used today in an eye bath to revive tired eyes. The plant has a scent like apricots and agrimony tea was sometimes drunk in France for its flavour as well as its medicinal virtues. A clinical study of the properties of tea made from *Agrimonia eupatoria* showed it has antioxidant and anti-inflammatory effects and improves lipid profile by increasing HDL cholesterol levels.[4] The plant was also traditionally added to mead to improve the flavour.

Another common name for agrimony is fairy's wand and it has long been considered powerfully magical. It was believed to be a cure for people who had been 'elf-shot' *i.e.* were suffering from a mystery illness.[5] It is still used in modern-day witchcraft. Placed under or in the pillow at night, agrimony leaves bring a deep, undisturbed sleep, particularly valuable to those whose minds are troubled.

The aerial parts of the plant are used today in herbal medicine to treat childhood diarrhoea and other digestive problems, appendicitis, mucous colitis, urinary infections, sore throats and wounds. The extract has a combination of astringency (it contains tannins) and bitterness (like gentian and centaury). At between 3 and 21% tannin content,[1] agrimony can be used for tanning leather. The whole plant produces a yellow dye, pale in autumn but darker later in the year.

**Fruits showing barbed hairs**

**Chemical diagram**

Agrimophol

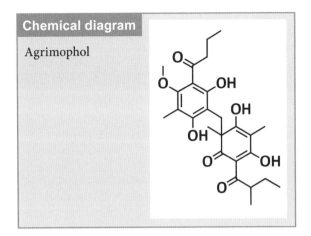

One of the plant's chemical constituents, agrimophol,[6] is used to expel parasitic worms from the bladder or intestine[7] and can treat taeniasis[8] and schistosomiasis.[9] Success rates of agrimophol or the plant extract used in Chinese medicine (*Agrimonia pilosa*, hairy agrimony) were over 94% in the treatment of taeniasis (tapeworm infestation).[8] It also acts against the organism which causes onchocerciasis *i.e.* river blindness (*Onchocerca volvulus*), many common bacteria such as *E. coli* and *Staphylococcus* and those related to dysentery, typhoid fever[7] and malaria.[10] The antiparasitic action involves inhibition of the metabolism of the parasites, leading to their death on contact with agrimophol.[10]

A study of the action of agrimophol against the bacterium causing tuberculosis suggests its action involves interfering with the bacterium's ability to maintain an acid-base balance. Thus, the intrabacterial pH can become acidic and the bacteria can't survive. This could be of use in the treatment of *Mycobacterium tuberculosis* infection as this bacterium is immune to current drugs.[11]

Agrimophol has a beneficial effect on patients being treated for lung cancer using radiotherapy.[12] It acts as a radiosensitiser on lung adenocarcinoma cells but does not affect development of radiopneumonitis and tumour distant metastasis *i.e.* it makes the target cells more sensitive to radiation but does not increase the occurrence of radiation-induced side-effects. At the same time, agrimophol can significantly reduce the incidence of pleural fluid and tumour relapse after radiotherapy.

One traditional use of agrimony is as an antidiabetic treatment and studies have indicated that an aqueous extract of *Agrimonia eupatoria* shows antihyperglycaemic action. This is believed to be associated with the stimulation of insulin secretion and augmentation of glucose uptake and metabolism by muscle. It behaves differently to type 2 diabetes drugs such as metformin which cause an insulin-mediated increase in peripheral glucose uptake and suppress glucose production by the liver.[13] The aqueous extract of agrimony also shows activity against the hepatitis B virus.[14]

## References:

1. F. Watkins, B. Pendry, A. Sanchez-Medina, O. Corcoran, (2012); Antimicrobial assays of three native British plants used in Anglo-Saxon medicine for wound healing formulations in 10th century England; *J. Ethnopharmacol.*, 144(2), 408–15; doi: 10.1016/j.jep.2012.09.031

2. http://arquebuse-water.com/ [Accessed 08.03.17]

3. S. Johnson, (20th December 2015); Plague Waters: A Medieval Cure for the Incurable; UWGB Commons; http://www.uwgbcommons.org/archives/32277 [Accessed 08.03.17]

4. D. Ivanova, D. Vankova, M. Nashar, (2013); *Agrimonia eupatoria* tea consumption in relation to markers of inflammation, oxidative status and lipid metabolism in healthy subjects; *Arch. Physiol. Biochem.*, 119(1), 32–7; doi: 10.3109/13813455.2012.729844

5. http://www.witchipedia.com/herb:agrimony [Accessed 08.03.17]

6. N.R. Farnsworth, O. Akerele, A.S. Bingel, D.D. Soejarto, Z. Guo, (1985); Medicinal plants in therapy; *Bull. World Health Organ.*, 63(6), 965–81; PMCID: PMC2536466

7. http://www.herbalextractsplus.com/agrimony.html [Accessed 17.09.17]

8. X. Peigen, C. Keji, (1988); Recent advances in clinical studies of Chinese medicinal herbs 2. Clinical trials of Chinese herbs in a number of chronic conditions; *Phytother. Res.*, 2(2), 55–62; doi: 10.1002/ptr.2650020202

9. J. You, W. Le, J. Mei, (1982); The in vitro effect of agrimophol on *Schistosoma japonicum*; *Acta Pharm. Sinic.*, 1982-09; http://en.cnki.com.cn/Article_en/CJFDTotal-YXXB198209004.htm [Accessed 09.03.17]

10. X.-Y. Zou, B. Ye, (2014); Traditional Chinese Treatment of Taeniasis; in *Treatment of Human Parasitosis in Traditional Chinese Medicine*; Eds. H. Mehlhorn, Z. Wu, B. Ye, Springer-Verlag Berlin Heidelberg, ISBN 978-3-642-39823, pp 155–68; doi: 10.1007/978-3-642-39824-7_10

11. C.M. Darby, H.I. Ingólfsson, X. Jiang, C. Shen, M. Sun, N. Zhao, K. Burns, G. Liu, S. Ehrt, J.D. Warren, O.S. Andersen, S.J. Brickner, C. Nathan, (2013); Whole Cell Screen for Inhibitors of pH Homeostasis in *Mycobacterium tuberculosis*; *PLoS ONE,* 8(7), e68942; doi: 10.1371/journal.pone.0068942

12. J. Han, X. Wang, Y. Wang, G. Li, Y. Han, Z. Yang, T. Yan, S. Hong, (2003); A clinical prospective study of radiosensitization on lung adenocarcinoma by agrimophol; *Chinese Journal of Radiological Medicine and Protection*, 2003, 23(5), 355–7; https://inis.iaea.org/search/search.aspx?orig_q=RN:35074436

13. A.M. Gray, P.R. Flatt, (1998); Actions of the traditional anti-diabetic plant, *Agrimony eupatoria* (agrimony): effects on hyperglycaemia, cellular glucose metabolism and insulin secretion; *Br. J. Nutr.*, 80(1), 109–14; doi: 10.1017/S0007114598001834

14. D.H. Kwon, H.Y. Kwon, H.J. Kim, E.J. Chang, M.B. Kim, S.K. Yoon, E.Y. Song, D.Y. Yoon, Y.H. Lee, I.S. Choi, Y.K. Choi, (2005); Inhibition of hepatitis B virus by an aqueous extract of *Agrimonia eupatoria* L.; *Phytother. Res.*, 19(4), 355–8; doi: 10.1002/ptr.1689

# Star of Bethlehem

## (*Ornithogalum umbellatum*)

Common (or garden) star of Bethlehem (*Ornithogalum umbellatum*) and other members of the genus are sometimes grown as ornamental plants. Flower stalks of *Ornithogalum thyrsoides* are placed in food dyes and the flowers take on the colour of the dye. The coloured flower heads are sold together with the authentic white flowers.[1] Star of Bethlehem's white, star-shaped flowers close at night and open only when there is sunshine, remaining closed on cloudy days; this is reflected in some of its common names like nap-at-noon, eleven-o'clock lady and sleepy dick. Petals have a characteristic green stripe on the underside.

Another name, dove's dung, was used by the Arabs, who sometimes ate the bulbs as a vegetable. Bulbs of the plant, also known as white field onion, were also eaten raw or cooked in the UK. However, large quantities can be poisonous both to grazing animals and to humans. Bulbs can also cause dermatitis on contact with the skin of sensitive people. A homoeopathic remedy was made from the bulbs to treat some types of cancer.

The only truly native species in the UK is *Ornithogalum pyrenaicum* or Pyrenees star of Bethlehem. This grew abundantly in woods near Bath where the young, unexpanded shoots were cooked and served like asparagus; hence, a common name for this plant is Bath asparagus.

Common star of Bethlehem, along with other European species of the genus, contains cardiac

**Star of Bethlehem** is the Bach flower remedy for shock.

glycosides. Extracts of the bulbs have a similar effect on the heart as extract of foxgloves (digitalis) does.[2] Specifically, this is to slow down the heart rate and strengthen the beats. Comparison with one of the active compounds found in digitalis, known as digitoxin, showed the extract caused less slowing of the heart, a greater diuretic effect and less gastrointestinal nausea.[2] The major active compound present is convallatoxin,[3] although fifteen other cardenolides have also been isolated (cardenolides are a class of cardiac glycosides). Convallatoxin has also shown activity against human lung cancer cells.[4] All parts of the plant contain cardiac glycosides but these are most concentrated in the bulbs. The convallatoxin content of the bulbs increases on defloration of the plant.[2] It is also present in lily of the valley (*Convallaria majalis*) which is used in herbal medicine to treat heart failure and oedema.

The genus name comes from the Greek words *ornis* meaning bird and *gala* meaning milk, in reference to the white flowers. The term 'bird's milk' was used by the Romans to indicate something wonderful.[1]

Many plants in the genus have been studied for their medicinal effects. The leaf extracts of the Turkish species *Ornithogalum alpigenum* are good free radical scavengers and bulb extracts show antifungal and antibacterial activities.[5] The aerial parts of *Ornithogalum cuspidatum* are used in Iran as a food additive and as an anti-irritant and relaxant taken

to soothe the throat and treat a dry cough. Tests on the properties of the methanol extract showed activity against human prostate cancer and fibrosarcoma cells.[6]

Extracts from the bulbs of *Ornithogalum thyrsoides*, which is common in South Africa, were found to be active against leukaemia.[7] One traditional use of the leaves was to make an infusion taken to treat type 1 diabetes.[1] The Afrikaans vernacular name of the plant is *tjienkerientjee*, a simulation of the chink sound made when fresh stalks are rubbed against one another by the wind. In English, this is translated as chincherinchee.[1]

The African species *Ornithogalum caudatum* has a number of synonyms. Among its common names are false sea onion and pregnant onion. It has a large bulb, growing mainly above the soil, on which bulblets grow beneath the skin then burst through and detach themselves.[8] Medicinally, it was used by the Zulu as an anti-inflammatory and in some places to treat diabetes.[2] Extracts from the bulbs cause a significant,

**Chemical diagram**

Convallatoxin

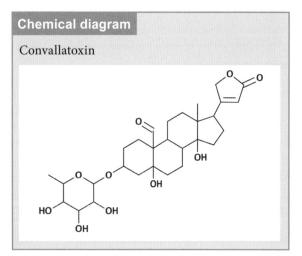

beneficial increase in glucose utilisation.[9] An extract is used in traditional Chinese medicine to treat cancer, as an antimicrobial and anti-inflammatory agent and to treat hepatitis and parotitis.[2] It has proven effects against breast[10] and liver[11] cancer. Several patents relating to the extraction and use of extracts to treat cancer and inflammation of the gall-bladder have been granted.[2]

In Christian folklore, it is said that *Ornithogalum arabicum* first appeared on the earth on the night of Christ's birth. According to the legend, the star that led the three wise men to Bethlehem burst into thousands of fragments after it had stopped at its destination. The bright fragments which fell to the ground were transformed into flowers to indicate the holiness of the area.[12]

## References:

1. Y. Singh, (2005); http://pza.sanbi.org/ornithogalum-thyrsoides [Accessed 11.03.17]

2. D.A. Mulholland, S.L. Schwikkard, N.R. Crouch, (2013); The chemistry and biological activity of the Hyacinthaceae; *Nat. Prod. Rep.*, 30(9), 1165–210; doi: 10.1039/c3np70008a

3. R.B. Kelly, E.G. Daniels, L.B. Spaulding, (1965); Cytotoxicity of Cardiac Principles; *J. Med. Chem.*, 8(4), 547–8; doi: 10.1021/jm00328a037

4. N.F.Z. Schneider, F.C. Geller, L. Persich, L.L. Marostica, R.M. Pádua, W.Kreis, F.C. Braga, C.M.O. Simões, (2016); Inhibition of cell proliferation, invasion and migration by the cardenolides digitoxigenin monodigitoxoside and convallatoxin in human lung cancer cell line; *Nat. Prod. Res.*, 30(11), 1327–31; doi: 10.1080/14786419.2015.1055265

5. A.A. Makasci, R. Mammadov, O. Dusen, H.I. Isik, (2010); Antimicrobial and antioxidant activities of medicinal plant species *Ornithogalum alpigenum* Stapf. from Turkey; *J. Med. Plants Res.*, 4(16), 1637–42; doi: 10.5897/JMPR10.087

6. H. Asadi, M. Orangi, D. Shanehbandi, Z. Babaloo, A. Delazar, L. Mohammadnejad, F. Zare Shahneh, S. Valiyari, B. Baradaran, (2014); Methanolic Fractions of *Ornithogalum cuspidatum* Induce Apoptosis in PC-3 Prostate Cancer Cell Line and WEHI-164 Fibrosarcoma Cancer Cell Line; *Adv. Pharm. Bull.*, 4(5), 455-8; doi: 10.5681/apb.2014.067

7. M. Kuroda, Y. Mimaki, K. Ori, H. Sakagami, Y. Sashida, (2004); Steroidal Glycosides from the Bulbs of *Ornithogalum thyrsoides*; *J. Nat. Prod.*, 67(10), 1690–6; doi: 10.1021/np040108i

8. http://www.llifle.com/Encyclopedia/SUCCULENTS/Family/Hyacinthaceae/19751/Ornithogalum_caudatum [Accessed 11.03.17]

9. M. van Huyssteen, P.J. Milne, E.E. Campbell; M. van de Venter, (2011); Antidiabetic And Cytotoxicity Screening Of Five Medicinal Plants Used By Traditional African Health Practitioners In The Nelson Mandela Metropole, South Africa; *Afr. J. Tradit. Complement. Altern. Med.*, 8(2), 150–8; PMCID: PMC3252689

10. X. Liu, Y. Zhang, (2012); Effect of *Ornithogalum caudatum* Ait. Saponins on Apoptosis of MDA-MB-231 Breast Cancer Cells and Its Mechanism; *Lishizhen Med. Mat. Med. Res.*, 23(6), 1388–90; http://en.cnki.com.cn/Article_en/CJFDTotal-SZGY201206029.htm [Accessed 11.03.17]

11. Z. Qu, X. Shi, X. Zou, Y. Ji, (2016); Study on the Apoptotic Mechanisms of Human Liver Cancer HepG-2 Cells Induced by Total Saponins of *Ornithogalum caudatum*; *J. Chin. Med. Mat.*, 2016(4), 867–71; https://caod.oriprobe.com/articles/50273837/Study_on_the_Apoptotic_Mechanisms_of_Human_Liver_C.htm [Accessed 11.03.17]

12. B. Roberson and J. Stokes, Jr., (1982); The Herbs and Flowers of the Virgin Mary; *The Herbarist*; https://udayton.edu/imri/mary/h/herbs-and-flowers-of-the-virgin-mary.php [Accessed 11.03.17]

**Partially open flowers showing green striped underside of petals**

# Clematis

*(Clematis vitalba)*

*Clematis vitalba* is sometimes known as old man's beard due to the white, fluffy tails attached to its seed pods. Alternatively, it is called traveller's joy, reputedly coined by the 16th century herbalist John Gerard, reflecting that clematis vines tend to grow in hedges by roads. In the autumn, he described clematis as 'decking and adorning waies and hedges where people trauell'.[1] The fresh, whole plant is toxic if taken internally but it does have some traditional uses. Dried winter stems were sometimes smoked instead of tobacco by the poor, leading to common names for the plant like smokewood and boy's bacca.[1] Stems, particularly after boiling, can be used in basketry and the fibres used to make rope.[1] After careful cooking to remove the toxins, clematis shoots can be eaten.[2]

As part of the buttercup family, the fresh plant contains protoanemonin, which is formed from ranunculin when the plant is under attack. If ingested, this causes a burning sensation in the mouth and throat, mouth ulcers, abdominal pain and nausea, vomiting and diarrhoea. Some traditional uses relied on this irritant effect; for example, bruised leaves were applied to the eyes to cause tears, to the throat to induce coughing or to the skin to cause inflammation or blisters. Reputedly, beggars sometimes rubbed leaves on their skin to cause blisters or ulcers which would elicit sympathy from passers-by,[2] leading to other common names like beggar's grass or beggar's plant.

Clematis was sometimes used as a headache cure. An Australian species, *Clematis glycinoides*, is known as

**Clematis** is the Bach flower remedy for those who day-dream about the future rather than living in the present.

headache vine.[3] The ammonia-like vapour from the crushed leaves was inhaled causing a severe reaction which rendered the headache pain forgotten. The reaction was described as the sensation of the head 'exploding', eyes 'watering' and severe irritation to the nasal passages.[3] Clematis was also used as a stimulant to bring around people who had fainted, perhaps after being in close proximity to a ghost or to remove 'ghost bullets' from the body.[4] It was used by Native Americans as a horse-stimulant.[5] The plants were utilised as counter-irritants, usually in a poultice, to treat conditions such as rheumatism.[3] Protoanemonin has antibacterial,[6] antifungal,[7] antimutagenic[8] and sedative effects.[9]

After drying or boiling, clematis contains no protoanemonin as this cyclodimerises to form the compound anemonin,[5] *i.e.* two molecules of protoanemonin (monomers) join together to form one molecule of

**Chemical diagram**

Protoanemonin

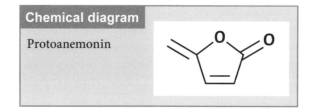

**Chemical diagram**

Anemonin

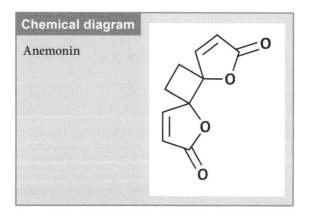

anemonin (the cyclodimer). This compound is non irritant and has anti-inflammatory,[10] antispasmodic,[11] antipyretic and sedative properties.[9] One potential use of anemonin is in the treatment of excess pigmentation of the skin; anemonin inhibits the tyrosinase family of proteins which are involved in the synthesis of the skin pigment melanin.[12] Anemonin is unstable and reacts with water to form a stable, non-toxic carboxylic acid.[11]

Traditional uses of dried clematis included to treat inflammatory conditions such as rheumatism and to reduce fever. Roots and stems of *Clematis vitalba* were boiled and taken in oil to treat itching and branches smoked to ease tooth pain. Clematis was also considered diuretic and diaphoretic and used to treat STDs.[3]

Chinese clematis (*Clematis chinensis*) is used as an anti-inflammatory analgesic in traditional Chinese medicine. It is also used when fish bones have been lodged in the throat. Combined with vinegar and brown sugar, it is found to soften the bone; a study of 104 cases of fish bone impaction treated with clematis showed an 85% success rate![3] 'Clematis vine', often *Clematis armandii*, *Chuan Mu Tong*, is used in China as a diuretic.[13] It contains the compound clematine.[14] A compound clematine was previously described as a violent poison found in *Clematis vitalba*, although it is unclear if this is the same compound as that identified in clematis vine.

A *Clematis vitalba* vine wrapped round a tree trunk

Medicinally important compounds are numerous in *Clematis* species. One important example in the dried aerial parts of *Clematis vitalba* is vitalboside.[15] One study states that this compound shows anti-inflammatory, antinociceptive (*i.e.* reducing sensitivity to pain) and antipyretic (fever-reducing) activities corresponding to the activity noted for the plant.[16]

*Clematis vitalba* can be invasive and is considered a plant pest in New Zealand and parts of the USA. Taken to New Zealand in the 1930s as a garden plant, it flourished in the country's warm and wet climate, smothering native plants. Reputedly, clematis does the Devil's work by invading other plants and choking them! In 1989, English naturalist David Bellamy fronted an advertising campaign stating, 'Old Man's Beard Must Go'![17] Killing the plant requires the vines to be cut twice, once at waist height and again at ground level. Only cutting at one or the other point allows the plant to regrow. All cut material must be burnt or buried to prevent re-growth and the remaining vine is left on the tree to dry out, to prevent damage to the host. The remaining stumps are treated with a specially formulated herbicide mix. Treatment must be repeated every year until re-growth is checked and the seed bank is emptied.[1]

**References:**

1. D. Morgan, (2002); Old Man's Beard - our native *Clematis*; http://www.countrysketches.co.uk/nature_notes/old_mans_beard.htm [Accessed 14.03.17]

2. A. Gulick, (19th April 2013); *Clematis Vitalba*: A Tasty Edible Weed, Only Slightly Poisonous; http://thebittersweetgourmet.com/clematis-vitalba-a-poisonous-and-tasty-perennial/ [Accessed 14.03.17]

3. C. Williams, (2014); Medicinal Plants in Australia Volume 4: An Antipodean Apothecary; Rosenberg Publishing, ISBN10 1925078086, pp 110–4

4. C.E. Turi, (3rd November 2016); Spiritual Uses of the Buttercup Family in North America; *Spiritual Botany*, issue 1; http://www.spiritualbotany.com/category/issue-1/ [Accessed 14.03.17]

5. J.R. Kern, J.H. Cardellina II, (1983); Native American medicinal plants. Anemonin from the horse stimulant *Clematis hirsutissima*; *J. Ethnopharmacol.*, 8(1), 121–3; doi: 10.1016/0378-8741(83)90093-4

6. N. Didry, L. Dubreuil, M. Pinkas, (1993); Microbiological properties of protoanemonin isolated from *Ranunculus bulbosus*; *Phytother. Res.*, 7(1), 21–4; doi: 10.1002/ptr.2650070107

7. M.L. Martín, L. San Román, A. Domínguez, (1990); In Vitro Activity of Protoanemonin, an Antifungal Agent; *Planta Med.*, 56(1), 66–9; doi: 10.1055/s-2006-960886

8. H. Minakata, H. Komura, K. Nakanishi, T. Kada, (1983); Protoanemonin, an antimutagen isolated from plants; *Mutat. Res./Genet. Tox.*, 116(3–4), 317–22; doi: 10.1016/0165-1218(83)90069-1

9. M.L. Martin, A.V.O. de Urbina, M.J. Montero, R. Carrón, L. San Roma, (1988); Pharmacologic effects of lactones isolated from *Pulsatilla alpina* subsp. *aphfolia*; *J. Ethnopharmacol.*, 24(2–3), 185–91; doi: 10.1016/0378-8741(88)90150-X

10. T.H. Lee, N.K. Huang, T.C. Lai, A.T.Y. Yang, G.J. Wang, (2008); Anemonin, from *Clematis crassifolia*, potent and selective inducible nitric oxide synthase inhibitor; *J. Ethnopharmacol.*, 116(3), 518–27; doi: 10.1016/j.jep.2007.12.019

11. M.C. Maior, C. Dobrotă, (2013); Natural compounds with important medical potential found in *Helleborus* sp.; *Cent. Eur. J. Biol.*, 8(3), 272–85; doi: 10.2478/s11535-013-0129-x

12. Y.-H. Huang, T.-H. Lee, K.-J. Chan, F.-L. Hsu, Y.-C. Wu, M.-H. Lee, (2008); Anemonin is a natural bioactive compound that can regulate tyrosinase-related proteins and mRNA in human melanocytes; *J. Dermatol. Sci.*, 49(2), 115–23; doi: 10.1016/j.jdermsci.2007.07.008

13. http://www.chineseherbshealing.com/clematis-vine/ [Accessed 16.03.17]

14. Y. Chen, J. Liu, R.S. Davidson, O.W. Howarth, (1993); Isolation and structure of clematine, a new flavanone glycoside from *Clematis armandii* Franch.; *Tetrahedron*, 49(23), 5169–76; doi: 10.1016/S0040-4020(01)81881-0

15. R. Chawla, S. Kumar, A. Sharma, (2012); The genus *Clematis* (Ranunculaceae): Chemical and pharmacological perspectives; *J. Ethnopharmacol.*, 143(1), 116–50; doi: 10.1016/j.jep.2012.06.014

16. E. Yesilada, E. Küpeli, (2007); *Clematis vitalba* L. aerial part exhibits potent anti-inflammatory, antinociceptive and antipyretic effects; *J. Ethnopharmacol.*, 110(3), 504–15; doi: 10.1016/j.jep.2006.10.016

17. https://www.nzonscreen.com/title/old-mans-beard-must-go-1989 [Accessed 16.03.17]

# Mustard

*(Sinapis arvensis)*

The name *Sinapis* originates from the Greek word *sinapi* for mustard. There are six species in the genus. *Sinapis arvensis* (wild mustard, field mustard or charlock) is often considered to be a weed, growing alongside commercial rapeseed (*Brassica napus*) crops. Rapeseed and charlock are part of the mustard/cabbage family (Brassicaceae) and both contain significant quantities of erucic acid. This is an omega-9 fatty acid and tests on animals in the 1970s suggested a possible link with the development of heart disease.[1] As a result, low erucic acid rapeseed (LEAR) or canola was developed. Canola is widely used, particularly in North America and Australia, but claims that it is beneficial to health remain controversial.[2,3] Although there is no conclusive evidence of health problems in humans from dietary ingestion of erucic acid, the quantity permitted in oils and foodstuffs containing these oils is limited to 5% (1% when intended for children) within the EU.[4]

Lorenzo's oil is a combination of the triglyceride forms of oleic acid and erucic acid (in a 4:1 ratio) from olive oil and rapeseed oil, respectively. The use of this oil as a treatment for adrenoleukodystrophy (ALD) was popularised by Augusto Odone. His son, Lorenzo, suffered from the condition, which causes a build-up of very long-chain fatty acids in the blood. ALD leads to brain damage and usually causes death within two years.[5]

A fictionalised version of the story was made into a Hollywood film in 1992, with the oil shown as a miracle cure. However, although the oil slows down

**Mustard** is the Bach flower remedy for those who feel depressed for no apparent reason.

progression of the disease, it is not a cure and patients do eventually die.[6] Lorenzo died in 2008, aged 30, 24 years after being diagnosed with ALD and given two years to live.[7] Although not a cure for patients already showing symptoms of ALD, the oil has been shown to delay the disease developing in people who have the ALD gene.[6,8] However, the presence of erucic acid has been linked to a reduction in both the number of platelets[9] and the number of white blood cells present in the blood,[10] so these have to be carefully monitored when using the oil.

Charlock has been used as a human and animal food source. The leaves can be eaten raw in salads when young, or cooked when older. The seeds can be sprouted and eaten raw or ground into a powder and used as a mustard-like flavouring. An edible oil can be extracted which also burns well. Charlock seed was a famine food in Scotland and was used to make a gritty bread when grain supplies dwindled.[11]

All types of mustard provide a rich source of selenium and magnesium. The former is beneficial in the treatment of asthma and rheumatism while the latter can cause a reduction in blood pressure and in the occurrence of migraine headaches.[12]

Charlock contains the compound sinalbin which was first found in the seeds of white mustard (*Sinapis alba*). Sinalbin reacts with an enzyme myrosinase, also found in the plant, to give 4-hydroxybenzyl isothiocyanate, a mustard oil. This is highly unstable and pungent, with a half-life at pH 3 of 321 minutes and at pH 6.5 of 6 minutes. It degrades to produce the almost odourless 4-hydroxybenzyl alcohol (gastrodigenin) and the isothiocyanate ion.[13] White mustard seeds are sometimes used to make the condiment known as mustard, but the flavour is much less pungent than that obtained using black mustard seeds (*Brassica nigra*). Seeds of charlock and white mustard are toxic in large quantities due to the production of isothiocyanates, but most birds can tolerate them.

Dried seeds of white mustard have rubefacient properties and were sometimes ground with black mustard seeds to make a flour used in poultices. A rubefacient is applied to the skin and causes reddening due to

## Chemical diagram

Sinalbin

the dilation of blood vessels which leads to increased blood flow. White mustard seeds were used to treat digestive disorders and at one time were a fashionable laxative, particularly for older people. However, there is a danger that seeds remain in the intestines where they can cause inflammation of the stomach and intestinal canal. An infusion of the seeds was used to treat rheumatism and bronchitis. Mustard seed tea was sometimes gargled to ease a sore throat.

The pungency of black mustard seeds is due to another compound, sinigrin, which is also present in Brussels sprouts and cabbage but not in charlock or white mustard seeds. Sinigrin reacts with myrosinase to produce compounds including the highly pungent allyl isothiocyanate. This activates the TRPA1 and TRPV1 receptors[14] (the receptor for irritants and stench and the capsaicin receptor, respectively) and causes a lachrymatory response (*i.e.* eyes watering!). It has potential for use as a cancer preventing agent.[15] Synthetic allyl isothiocyanate is used as a food-flavouring, antibacterial agent and insecticide.[16]

Compounds produced by the action of myrosinase on sinalbin or sinigrin cause damage to the plant so are present in a safe form and are only released when the plant is under attack. Myrosinase is kept in a separate compartment to sinalbin or sinigrin and the compounds only come into contact when the

cell walls between them are damaged by cutting or chewing (or if the seeds or leaves are crushed). This behaviour is like that shown in garlic, where alliin and allinase are separated in the plant but on contact react to form the highly reactive compound allicin.

Black mustard seeds are used in herbal medicine on the skin or in a bath to stimulate circulation and reduce skeletal or muscular pain. They are also used as a diaphoretic (*i.e.* to cause perspiration) and to treat colds, influenza and bronchitis. Mustard was held in high regard by Ancient Greek physicians for the medicinal action of its seeds and they attributed its discovery to Asclepius, god of medicine.

A condiment made from mustard has been popular for thousands of years and was used by both the Ancient Greeks and the Romans. In the Middle Ages, French monks generated a large amount of income by selling mustard. Pope John XXII of Avignon (1249 –1334) loved mustard so much that he created the post of '*Grand Moutardier du Pape*' (Grand Mustard-Maker to the Pope). He gave the job to his nephew who lived near Dijon and the town soon became the mustard-making capital of the world. To prepare mustard, the seeds are crushed and the hulls and bran removed. The remaining powder is mixed with liquids such as vinegar or wine, then salt and other spices or flavourings added.[17]

In Denmark and India, it was believed that spreading mustard seeds around the exterior of the home would

**Mustard seeds**

keep out evil spirits. The ancient Chinese considered mustard to be an aphrodisiac. In German folklore, a bride was advised to sew mustard seeds into the hem of her wedding dress to assure her dominance of the household.[17]

## References:

1. *e.g.* A.M.M. Abdellatif, (1972); Cardiopathogenic Effects of Dietary Rapeseed Oil; *Nutr. Rev.*, 30(1), 2–6; doi: 10.1111/j.1753-4887.1972.tb03965.x

2. L. Lin, H. Allemekinders, A. Dansby, L. Campbell, S. Durance-Tod, A. Berger, P.J.H. Jones, (2013); Evidence of health benefits of canola oil; *Nutr. Rev.*, 71(6), 370–85; doi: 10.1111/nure.12033

3. S. Fallon, M.G. Enig, (28th July 2002); The Great Con-ola; https://www.westonaprice.org/health-topics/know-your-fats/the-great-con-ola/ [Accessed 22.03.17]

4. http://eur-lex.europa.eu/legal-content/EN/ALL/?uri=uriserv:OJ.L_.2014.184.01.0001.01.ENG [Accessed 22.03.17]

5. http://myelin.org/lorenzos-oil/ [Accessed 22.03.17]

6. BBC News, (21st July 2004); Lorenzo's oil: The full story; http://news.bbc.co.uk/1/hi/health/3907559.stm [Accessed 22.03.17]

7. BBC News, (31st May 2008); Lorenzo's Oil boy is dead at 30; http://news.bbc.co.uk/1/hi/world/americas/7429221.stm [Accessed 22.03.17]

8. H.W. Moser, A.B. Moser, K. Hollandsworth, N.H. Brereton, G.V. Raymond, (2007); "Lorenzo's oil" therapy for X-linked adrenoleukodystrophy: rationale and current assessment of efficacy; *J. Mol. Neurosci.*, 33(1), 105–13; doi: 10.1007/s12031-007-0041-4

9. W.H. Zinkham, T. Kickler, J. Borel, H.W. Moser, (1993); Lorenzo's Oil and Thrombocytopenia in Patients with Adrenoleukodystrophy; *N. Engl. J. Med.*, 328(15), 1126–7; doi: 10.1056/NEJM199304153281513

10. C.J. Unkrig, R. Schroder, R.E. Scharf, (1994); Lorenzo's Oil and Lymphocytopenia; *N. Engl. J. Med.*, 330(8), 577; doi: 10.1056/NEJM199402243300819

11. http://www.thewesternisles.co.uk/wildflowers/charlock.htm [Accessed 23.03.17]

12. http://www.whfoods.com/genpage.php?tname=food-spice&dbid=106 [Accessed 23.03.17]

13. V. Borek, M.J. Morra, (2005); Ionic Thiocyanate (SCN-) Production from 4-Hydroxybenzyl Glucosinolate Contained in *Sinapis alba* Seed Meal; *J. Agric. Food Chem.*, 53(22), 8650–4; doi: 10.1021/jf051570r

14. W. Everaerts, M. Gees, Y.A. Alpizar, R. Farre, C. Leten, A. Apetrei, I. Dewachter, F. van Leuven, R. Vennekens, D. De Ridder, B. Nilius, T. Voets, K. Talavera, (2011); The Capsaicin Receptor TRPV1 Is a Crucial Mediator of the Noxious Effects of Mustard Oil; *Curr. Biol.*,21(4), 316–21; doi: 10.1016/j.cub.2011.01.031

15. Y. Zhang, (2010); Allyl isothiocyanate as a cancer chemopreventive phytochemical; *Mol. Nutr. Food Res.*, 54(1), 127–35; doi: 10.1002/mnfr.200900323

16. Pesticide Research Institute, (3rd October 2014); Technical Evaluation Report for the USDA National Organic Program; https://www.ams.usda.gov/sites/default/files/media/Allyl%20Isothiocyanate%20TR.pdf [Accessed 23.03.17]

17. http://www.thenibble.com/reviews/main/condiments/history-of-mustard.asp [Accessed 23.03.17]

# Chicory

## (*Cichorium intybus*)

Common chicory (*Cichorium intybus*) is also known as succory, coffeeweed or monk's beard. In Germany, it is sometimes called watcher of the road, recalling the legend of a girl who waited in vain by the roadside for the return of her lover and, exhausted, sank onto a patch of chicory and died. One version has her wearing his favourite blue dress which became the colour of the flowers. Chicory is often found growing by roads.

The leaves were believed to provide invincibility and were attached to banners carried by those visiting or exploring new territories for good luck. For this reason, gold prospectors during the California Gold Rush in the 19th century sometimes carried chicory leaves. The juice was also said to bring social success, as described in Dyets Dry Dinner of 1599, 'The body annoynted with the juyce of chicory is very available to obtain the favour of great persons'.[1]

Chicory was eaten in salads, cooked as a vegetable and used as a medicinal plant by the Egyptians, Greeks and Romans. In France, the forced foliage was termed *barbe de capucin*. The leaves were used to make a blue dye. Common chicory is related to endive (*Cichorium endivia*) which is also a salad vegetable and used medicinally. It is also in the same family as the dandelions (genus *Taraxacum*) with which it shares some properties and uses.

Chicory root was roasted and ground for use as a coffee substitute in Napoleonic times, when coffee supplies were limited. In France, the drink became known as

**Chicory** is the Bach flower remedy for possessiveness.

*café aux Chinoise* or *café aux Indiens*. It was believed to be a *contra-stimulante*, balancing the stimulating effects of coffee and was particularly valued as a drink for bilious people. Medicinally, the root was used as a tonic to increase the flow of bile, to aid the liver and digestion, as a diuretic, to kill parasitic worms and for constipation.

The flowers were used to make an eyewash to soothe inflammation. 'Violet plates', sweet confections shaped as tablets which were taken in the 17th century, contained chicory flowers as well as violets. They were said to be 'most pleasant and wholesome' and to 'comforteth the heart and inward parts'. The tablets were sometimes added to soups and stews.

Flowers open and close at regular times, regardless of the weather or season (in Britain, they open at 6 or 7 am and close just after midday). This behaviour defines chicory as one of the aequinoctales, as classified by Carl Linnaeus.[2] Other classes of flowers are meteorici (change opening times according to the weather) and tropici (change opening times according to the length of the day). Only aequinoctales are of value in flower clocks and Linnaeus proposed chicory as one of the plants in his flower clock when he was in Uppsala (where chicory flowers open at 4 or 5 am and close at 10 am).

Today, varieties of chicory are cultivated mainly for the leaves for salads (*e.g.* radicchio, red chicory) or for the roots (*Cichorium intybus* var. *sativum*) for use as a coffee substitute or adulterant. Camp coffee, available since 1885, contains about 25% chicory essence along with water, sugar and coffee essence. When mixed with coffee, chicory makes the drink more bitter and darker in colour. First produced by R. Paterson & Sons in Glasgow, Camp coffee was named after Campbell Paterson who devised the product. He also developed a range of cordials and fruit wines including a raspberry vinegar. This proved a popular mixer for whisky, aimed at the female palate and the drink was commonly referred to as 'Cuddle-Me-Dearie'. Before the advent of instant coffee, the preparation of coffee was cumbersome and time-consuming, involving grinding the beans before brewing. Camp coffee is a liquid essence and can consistently be prepared at a moment's notice. This is alluded to in the brand's slogan 'Ready Aye Ready'[3] (with 'aye' meaning always).

One driving force for its development was the need for an easily brewed drink for use in military camps and since its inception, Camp coffee has had connections with the military. The traditional design of the bottle label showed a Sikh serving a seated Highland soldier with the drink from a tray. However, after accusations that this was offensive (even 'obscene')[4] and outdated, the label was changed. Firstly, the tray was removed and today the label shows the Sikh and the Highland soldier sitting side-by-side enjoying the drink![5] The soldier is said to have been modelled on Sir Hector MacDonald, known as Fighting Mac, a Gordon Highlander and hero of the Boer War. He shot himself in 1903 after being accused of committing homosexual acts.

Camp coffee remained popular even after the introduction of instant coffee and sales trebled between 1939 and the early 1950s. Although other essences were available, Camp was the market leader, with sales equal to those of all the other brands combined.[3] Later, dwindling sales were temporarily revived when, in 1975, a severe frost in Brazil caused coffee prices to double. Today, the essence is produced by US giant McCormick Foods and is mainly used in baking when a coffee flavour is required.

**Radicchio**

Lactucin

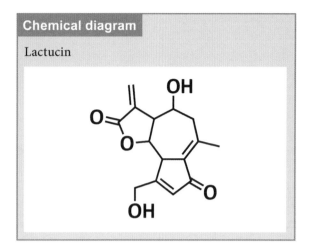

Two major bitter principles in chicory are lactucin and lactucopicrin, which are also found in wild lettuce (*Lactuca virosa*) and dandelion roots. Both compounds have demonstrable antimalarial activity[6] as well as acting as analgesics and sedatives.[7]

The Ancient Greeks sometimes ate lettuce soup at the end of a meal to help then sleep afterwards. In parts of Europe, lettuce is still served at the end of a meal. The Roman Emperor Domitian (51–96 CE) used the properties of lettuce for his amusement. He reputedly tortured guests, who were forbidden from sleeping in his presence, by serving large quantities of lettuce at the beginning of State dinners![8]

In wild lettuce, lactucin and lactucopicrin occur in the latex (a milky fluid secreted by the plant), which is sometimes known as lactucarium (or lettuce opium). This has been used as a drug for at least 1,000 years, mainly as a substitute for opium.[9]

Lactucarium is occasionally used today as a legal high although, reputedly, its misuse can result in death.[9] A report on the oral toxicity suggests its effects can include urine retention, dilated pupils, dizziness and anxiety.[10] Other authors report that injecting the extract can cause fever, abdominal pain and headaches.[11]

Eating wild lettuce can supposedly cause rabbits to become intoxicated. Beatrix Potter used this idea in her book 'The Tale of the Flopsy Bunnies' when two rabbits fall asleep after eating too much lettuce, 'It is said that the effect of eating too much lettuce is 'soporific''.[8] And lettuce was the subject of a rabbit-related health scare in 2016. Although commercially sold lettuce contains less lactucarium than wild lettuce does, it was reported that feeding rabbits lettuce, particularly iceberg lettuce, caused sedation and euphoria and could be dangerous.[12] Although the potential harm may have been overstated, it is probably best to avoid feeding lettuce to rabbits.[13]

The bitter compounds in chicory and lettuce come from a class of compounds known as sesquiterpene lactones, commonly found in plants in the daisy family (Asteraceae). They may be present to protect the plants from herbivores and/or microbes, the latter by disrupting the microbe's cell membranes. A study of chicory extract showed that it reduces the production of prostaglandins by inhibiting the COX-2 enzyme. This gives it anti-inflammatory and anticancer effects. The mechanism of action is unclear but the compound 8-deoxylactucin is considered to be the most active.[14]

**References:**

1. H. Butts, (1599); Dyets dry dinner consisting of eight seuerall courses; http://name.umdl.umich.edu/A17373.0001.001 [Accessed 24.04.17]

2. Coturnix, (23rd May 2007); A Blog Around the Clock; http://scienceblogs.com/clock/2007/05/23/carolus-linnaeus-floral-clocks/ [Accessed 24.04.17]

3. C. Foreman, (2004); "Made in Scotland" Household Names That Began in Scotland; Birlinn Ltd., Edinburgh, ISBN 1841582891, pp 23–4

4. BBC News, (1st August 1999); Coffee logo stirs racism row; http://news.bbc.co.uk/1/hi/uk/409264.stm [Accessed 24.04.17]

5. R. Pool; A History of the World; http://www.bbc.co.uk/ahistoryoftheworld/objects/XG1CiGSCTzqb05nDwIhhjg [Accessed 24.04.17]

6. T.A. Bischoff, C.J. Kelley, Y. Karchesy, M. Laurantos, P. Nguyen-Dinh, A.G. Arefi, (2004); Antimalarial activity of Lactucin and Lactucopicrin: sesquiterpene lactones isolated from *Cichorium intybus* L.; *J. Ethnopharmacol.*, 95(2–3), 455–7; doi: 10.1016/j.jep.2004.06.031

7. A. Wesołowska, A. Nikiforuk, K. Michalskab, W. Kisiel, E. Chojnacka-Wójcik, (2006); Analgesic and sedative activities of lactucin and some lactucin-like guaianolides in mice; *J. Ethnopharmacol.*, 107(2), 254–8; doi: 10.1016/j.jep.2006.03.003

8. L.L. Haupt, (15th June 2009); Soporific Salads and Lettuce Opium; The Tangled Nest; https://thetanglednest.com/2009/06/soporific-salads-and-lettuce-opium/ [Accessed 24.04.17]

9. S.A. Péter, (23rd November 2015); Simon's Wild Lettuce (*Lactuca Virosa*) Guide; https://simonsblogpark.com/legalhigh/simons-wild-lettuce-lactuca-virosa-guide/ [Accessed 24.04.17]

10. S. Besharat, M. Besharat, A. Jabbari, (2009); Wild lettuce (*Lactuca virosa*) toxicity; *BMJ Case Rep.*, 2009: bcr06.2008.0134; doi: 10.1136/bcr.06.2008.0134

11. M.E. Mullins, B.Z. Horowitz, (1998); The case of the salad shooters: intravenous injection of wild lettuce extract; *Vet. Hum. Toxicol.*, 40(5), 290–1; PMID: 9778767

12. H. Gye, (22nd June 2016); Don't feed rabbits lettuce because it contains a chemical that gets them STONED, pet owners are warned; Mail Online; http://www.dailymail.co.uk/news/article-3653981/Don-t-feed-rabbits-lettuce-contains-chemical-gets-stoned.html [Accessed 25.04.17]

13. T. Hale, (23rd June 2016); Does Lettuce Actually Get Your Rabbit Stoned?; http://www.iflscience.com/plants-and-animals/does-lettuce-actually-get-your-rabbit-stoned/ [Accessed 25.04.17]

14. M. Chadwick, H. Trewin, F. Gawthrop, C. Wagstaff, (2013); Sesquiterpenoids Lactones: Benefits to Plants and People; *Int. J. Mol. Sci.*, 14(6), 12780–5; doi: 10.3390/ijms140612780

# Vine

## (*Vitis vinifera*)

The name vine comes from the Latin *viere*, to twist, referring to the vine twining around trees or other supports. Elm trees were traditionally used to provide structures for vines to climb on in vineyards. Vines can live for 600 years and the stems of old plants can reach diameters of over 30 cm when they are useful as timber. In contrast to the wild grape vine (*Vitis vinifera* subsp. *sylvestris* or *Vitis sylvestris*) which has male and female flowers on different plants and so requires pollination before fruit is produced, the common domesticated vine, *Vitis vinifera*, is hermaphroditic.

The fruit, or grapes, can be eaten raw, dehydrated to form sultanas, currants or raisins, or the juice drunk or fermented to produce wine. The terms raisin, currant and sultana are defined differently depending where you are in the world. A raisin is basically any dried grape[1] but the following refers to the UK definitions. Sultanas and raisins come from different varieties of green grapes but, while raisins are black, sultanas are a golden colour. Sultanas originally came from Turkish sultana grapes but today the name is applied to any golden-coloured, dried seedless grape and the colour may be the result of treatment with sulfur dioxide![3] This retards enzymatic browning by PPO[2] (as is seen in apples; see crab apple section for more details) and may reduce loss of vitamin C.[1]

Raisins have small seeds but sultanas come from seedless grapes so have none. Both sultanas and raisins readily absorb liquids so are often soaked in alcohol or other liquids before use in baking. True

**Vine** is the Bach flower remedy for those who are dominant, strong-willed and inflexible.

currants don't come from grapes at all, but are black or red currants from currant bushes. However, the name Corinth raisin, referring to a dried red Corinth grape, was corrupted to currant. These have a dark colour similar to raisins but are about a quarter of the size.[4] After harvest, the grapes are dried, often with the aid of a dip made up of potassium carbonate and ethyl esters of fatty acids. This speeds up the drying process and, for sultanas, helps retain their golden colour. Traditionally olive oil and wood ash were used to aid drying.[2]

The sugar in grapes is D-glucose (dextrose or grape sugar). As this doesn't require to be broken down by enzymes in saliva before it's absorbed, it reaches the bloodstream quickly. It was traditionally used during convalescence and is the reason why today grapes are often given as a gift to those in hospital.

Vine leaves can be wrapped around a variety of fillings to give dolma or sarma, commonly eaten in the

Middle East, the Balkans and Central Asia. The leaves are astringent as they contain tannins and were used to staunch bleeding and for haemorrhages. The sap of the vine was used to treat weak eyes. Grapes were taken to increase flow of urine, to treat anaemia and small-pox and in cases of neuralgia and sleeplessness. Grapes have an adverse effect on the kidneys of dogs and even small amounts can cause kidney failure.[5] Raisins are slightly laxative, demulcent (soothing, particularly to mucous membranes) and nutritive.

The so-called 'grape cure' involved eating large quantities of grapes (approx. 1.3–2.7 kg/day); unripe grapes were taken for liver disease and ripe, sweet grapes for those with tissue wastage. In the 1920's, the Brandt Grape Cure was popularised by Johanna Brandt as a cure for certain types of cancer.[6] Many variations of the diet have been detailed but basically the treatment involves a mixture of water fasting and eating grapes. The basis is that, after fasting, the cancer cells consume a large amount of the sugary grapes quickly, so taking in significant quantities of the cytotoxic compounds they contain. The controversial treatment is not recommended by the American Cancer Society[7] but some who have tried it claim it has improved or even cured their condition.[8]

Johanna Brandt (1876–1964) was a South African who organised woman to spy on British officers and hid escaped Boer prisoners during the second British-Boer War (1899–1902).[9] She highlighted conditions in a British concentration camp, Irene, in a book and also to British journalist W.T. Stead.[10] His article on the subject may have helped turn public opinion in Britain against the war. Stead died in 1912, a passenger on HMS Titanic. After the war, Brandt became involved in Afrikaner politics and co-founded the Women's Party in 1915.[9]

Some chemical compounds in grapes have shown potential for use in cancer treatment. These include the related compounds resveratrol and piceatannol, which has an additional hydroxy (–OH) group.[11] Both have a range of potential medicinal benefits including as antioxidants and anti-inflammatory agents as well as in the prevention and treatment of cancer. They

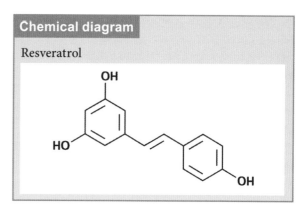

**Chemical diagram**

Resveratrol

occur in grape skins and, to a lesser extent, in their seeds. Resveratrol is produced by the plant in response to injury and protects it against fungi, bacteria and UV radiation.[12] Grape seed extract is sometimes taken as a food supplement to treat cardiovascular disease, poor circulation, diabetes-related eye conditions and high cholesterol[13] and has activity against some types of cancer.[14] Seedless grapes are popular as table grapes but these lose some of the possible medicinal benefits through their lack of seeds.

Resveratrol occurs in larger quantities in red wine than in white as red grapes are fermented along with their skins. The consumption of relatively more red wine in France than in the USA is one possible explanation for the so-called French paradox. This highlighted a relatively low incidence of coronary heart disease in France despite a relatively high consumption of saturated fats. There are many other suggestions to explain the paradox including the increased consumption of vitamin K2, greater intake of procyanidins, less stress or a mixture of factors. It may be as simple as the under-reporting of the condition in France or a time-lag between a change in saturated

fat consumption and its effect on heart health.[15] To maximise the possible benefits of resveratrol from red wine it should be sipped slowly as resveratrol is inactivated in the gut and liver so most does not reach the bloodstream. However, the quantity can be 100 times greater if the wine is sipped, as resveratrol can enter the blood *via* the mucous membranes in the mouth.[16]

The Ancient Egyptians considered wine to be the tears of the god Horus and it has been consumed for at least 6,000 years. The Greek god of wine was Dionysus or in Roman mythology, Bacchus. Most wine is made using varieties of *Vitis vinifera*. Initially, it was probably made by accident; grapes contain sugar and juice that readily starts to ferment in the presence of wild yeast, which is sometimes found on the skin of the grapes themselves. When wine began to be produced on purpose, grapes were sometimes crushed by trampling with bare feet to yield the juice. This made use of any fungi on the feet to instigate the fermentation

process. At first, the popularity of wine was partly due to the lack of clean drinking water and also to its association with Christianity. In the Bible, a little wine is recommended to help digestion and it is taken to represent the blood of Christ during communion.

Carlo Cignozzi, the owner of a vineyard in Tuscany, advocates playing music to the vines to make them stronger and healthier. A committed organic farmer, Carlo believes music of certain frequencies (100–400 MHz) deters pathogen attack.[17] In his vineyard, an array of 80 loudspeakers play Mozart's music 24 hours a day. Carlo reports that insects, birds and even wild boar are repelled and he believes the grapes have a higher sugar and polyphenol content and lower acidity. The grapes nearest the speakers grow 50% larger and mature two weeks earlier...and can even be seen growing towards the music.[18] Carlo likens the effect to tales of French friars in the Middle Ages who placed cattle stalls near the choir stalls 'because with Gregorian chant, the cows made more and better milk'.[18] And the music continues to have an effect during the wine-making process, normalising the timing of the second fermentation stage.[19]

Today, the health benefits of wine are still promoted but this is tempered with the knowledge of the potential damage of excessive alcohol consumption. Claimed benefits of moderate consumption include the prevention of lung and prostate cancers and dementia, a reduction in blood pressure and depression and the improvement of heart health.[20]

**An old vineyard in Tuscany**

## References:

1. https://mywellbeingjournal.com/2016/05/27/whats-the-difference-raisins-vs-currants-vs-sultanas/ [Accessed 26.04.17]

2. L.P. Christensen, W.L. Peacock; The Raisin Drying Process; http://iv.ucdavis.edu/files/24413.pdf [Accessed 28.04.17]

3. http://www.differencebetween.info/difference-between-raisins-sultanas-and-currants [Accessed 26.04.17]

4. http://www.thekitchn.com/whats-the-difference-between-raisins-sultanas-and-currants-223285 [Accessed 26.04.17]

5. P.A. Eubig, M.S. Brady, S.M. Gwaltney-Brant, S.A. Khan, E.M. Mazzaferro, C.M.K. Morrow, (2005); Acute Renal Failure in Dogs After the Ingestion of Grapes or Raisins: A Retrospective Evaluation of 43 Dogs (1992–2002); *J. Vet. Intern. Med.*, 19(5), 663–74; doi: 10.1111/j.1939-1676.2005.tb02744.x

6. J. Brandt, (2013); The Grape Cure; www.snowballpublishing.com, ISBN 978-1607966586

7. American Cancer Society, (1974); Grape diet; *CA: Cancer J. Clin.*, 24(3), 144–6; doi: 10.3322/canjclin.24.3.144

8. M. Moore, (1998); A Chemist on Grapes, Nutrition and the Bible; Women Confront Cancer: Twenty-One Leaders Making Medical History by Choosing Alternative and Complementary Therapies, eds. M.J. Wooddell, D.J. Hess, New York University Press, New York, United States, ISBN 081473586X, pp 179–88

9. I. Hexham, (1987); Modernity or Reaction in South Africa: The Case of Afrikaner Religion; Modernity and Religion, ed. W. Nicholls, Wilfrid Laurier Univ. Press, ISBN 0889201544, pp 62–88

10. W.T. Stead, (January 1902); Our Death Camps in South Africa; The Review of Reviews, vol. XXV, p 8; http://www.attackingthedevil.co.uk/reviews/death_camps.php [Accessed 29.04.17]

11. H. Piotrowska, M. Kucinska, M. Murias, (2012); Biological activity of piceatannol: leaving the shadow of resveratrol; *Mutat. Res. Rev. Mutat. Res.*, 750(1), 60–82; doi: 10.1016/j.mrrev.2011.11.001

12. J. Higdon, V.J. Drake, B. Delage, J.C. Espín, (2005, last update 6/11/15); Resveratrol; Micronutrient Information Center, Linus Pauling Institute, Oregon State University; http://lpi.oregonstate.edu/mic/dietary-factors/phytochemicals/resveratrol [Accessed 29.04.17]

13. M. Kaur, C. Agarwal, R. Agarwal, (2009); Anticancer and Cancer Chemopreventive Potential of Grape Seed Extract and Other Grape-Based Products; *J. Nutr.*, 139(9), 1806S–12S; doi: 10.3945/jn.109.106864

14. http://www.webmd.com/diet/grape-seed-extract [Accessed 23.09.17]

15. M. Law, N. Wald, (1999); Why heart disease mortality is low in France: the time lag explanation; *BMJ*, 318(7196),

**Leaves in autumn**

1471–80; doi: 10.1136/bmj.318.7196.1471

16. http://www.madehow.com/knowledge/Wine.html [Accessed 29.04.17]

17. C. Barnes, (13th February 2014); Does Playing Classical Music to Vines Make for Better Wine?; Grape Collective Magazine; https://grapecollective.com/articles/does-playing-classical-music-to-vines-make-for-better-wine [Accessed 28.04.17]

18. A. Josephy, (25th October 2012); A wine with notes of cherry… and Mozart; http://www.theflorentine.net/food-wine/2012/10/a-wine-with-notes-of-cherry-and-mozart/ [Accessed 28.04.17]

19. B. Wedeman, (10th June 2013); Where Mozart makes wine taste better; CNN; https://www.youtube.com/watch?v=u0B0wIQf9JA&feature=youtu.be [Accessed 28.04.17]

20. Y. Brazier, (updated 7th September 2017); Wine: Health Benefits and Health Risks; Medical News Today; http://www.medicalnewstoday.com/articles/265635.php [Accessed 23.09.17]

# Honeysuckle

## (*Lonicera caprifolium*)

Honeysuckles are shrubs or climbing plants (often growing in hedgerows) which climb *via* bines, *i.e.* their shoots grow in a helix around a support. Sometimes known as woodbine, this name comes from wood-bind, referring to their attachment to wood. When honeysuckle winds around tree branches it causes the branches to become twisted and these were sometimes used to make decorative walking sticks. The name honeysuckle may be linked to the tradition of children sucking nectar through the narrow end of the flower tube.

*Caprifolium* means goats' leaf, possibly referring to the plants being a favourite food of goats or to the resemblance of the leaves to goats' ears. The species is commonly known as Italian honeysuckle and is native to mid- and southern Europe. In the UK the species *Lonicera periclymenum* is more common. Italian honeysuckle is sometimes known as perfoliate honeysuckle and can be distinguished by its perfoliate upper leaves. These have the appearance of being passed through by the stem, as each leaf completely surrounds it. The flowers are cream-coloured, sometimes tinged with pink. Honeysuckles produce orange or red berries after flowering and the toxicity of these varies with species.

Honeysuckle is best known for its fragrance. Flowers are almost odourless during the day but release their fragrance at night to attract night-flying moths. This behaviour persists even when the flowers are cut. Moths feed through the flower tubes while hovering like hummingbirds and can detect the presence of

**Honeysuckle** is the Bach flower remedy for those who are living in the past.

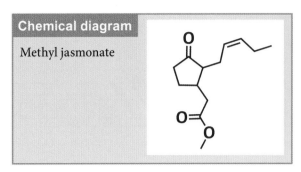

**Chemical diagram**

Methyl jasmonate

honeysuckle from a quarter of a mile away. The smell comes from a complex mixture of compounds which varies between species. These include linalool, the terpene ocimene, the sesquiterpenes germacrene D and α-farnesene and jasmonoids such as methyl jasmonate, jasmin lactone and jasmone.[1]

Linalool is found in many plants including the mints and lavender and is used in 60–80% of perfumed cosmetics, washing products and household cleaning products.[2] There are two related forms (stereoisomers) which have different smells, (R)-(−)-linalool (woody, found *e.g.* in lavender) and (S)-(+)-linalool (floral, found *e.g.* in sweet orange).[3] Linalool shows stress-reducing and sleep-promoting properties when inhaled and can fight depression and inflammation.[4,5] It also acts as an insecticide. However, the products of oxidation in air cause an allergic reaction in between 5 and 7% of eczema sufferers (or 2% of the whole population).[2] As well as possessing cytotoxic properties itself, linalool improves the efficacy of doxorubicin by reducing resistance to the drug in some breast cancer cells. It may have potential for use in the treatment of multi-drug resistant tumours.[6]

When honeysuckle is under attack, methyl jasmonate is released, signalling to nearby plants and thereby stimulating the production of defensive chemicals. It might also be involved in producing compounds to attract predators of the attackers.[7] Potential commercial uses include to increase the production of the anticancer drug paclitaxel from cell cultures.[8] Methyl jasmonate has also been found to reduce chilling injury and the growth of mould in fruits like strawberries and to stop bananas turning brown so could be used to improve their shelf-lives.[7]

Germacrene D and farnesol are found in large quantities in the volatile oil obtained from *Lonicera caprifolium* grown in Romania.[9] Although honeysuckles produce many volatile compounds, the importance of germacrene D in inciting interaction with one type of moth has been proven. It was shown to activate highly-sensitive, specialised receptor neurons on the antennae of female *Heliothis virescens* (tobacco budworm) moths suggesting it acts as a chemical cue to interaction.[10] Germacrene D is common to many plant species and a variety of roles have been suggested for it including to kill mosquitos, to repel aphids and ticks and as a precursor to other compounds.[11]

Farnesol is a sesquiterpene alcohol with potential use in the treatment of wounds by disrupting the

formation of biofilms. These are made up of microbial or fungal cells surrounded by a polymeric matrix that protects the cells and helps them adhere to natural surfaces.[12] Studies of the action of farnesol on the fungus *Candida albicans* have shown that the process of filamentation of the fungal cells is disrupted by farnesol, inhibiting biofilm formation.[13] The presence of biofilms delays wound healing and these are present in most chronic wounds. The addition of farnesol to wound dressings can, therefore, aid healing.[12]

There are around 180 species of honeysuckle, some of which have been or are currently used medicinally.

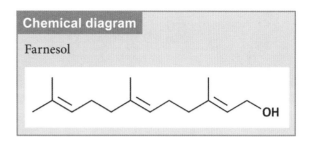

**Chemical diagram**

Farnesol

Honeysuckle leaves and flowers were used to relieve pain and inflammation (they contain salicylates) and extracts from the leaves were taken for their antibacterial and antiviral properties and to treat conditions of the liver and spleen. The plants were used as a treatment for respiratory conditions such as asthma and also for their astringent, expectorant, laxative and diuretic properties. They were sometimes applied externally to treat skin conditions.

Japanese honeysuckle (*Lonicera japonica, Jin Yin Hua*) is used in traditional Chinese medicine to treat colds, flu and sore throats. It is used in combination with three other herbs as a treatment for swine flu[14] and also has anti-inflammatory activity.[15] Research has shown that the plant is effective in combination with other herbs as a treatment for acute bronchitis.[16] A potent antiviral molecule found in a decoction of Japanese honeysuckle, called MIR2911, has been identified as 'a virological penicillin'. It directly targets various strains of the influenza A virus including H1N1 (swine flu) and H5N1 (avian flu) and inhibits replication, acting as a preventative as well as a therapeutic agent.[17,18]

Honeysuckle is a symbol of fidelity and affection but, in Victorian times, young girls were forbidden to bring it into the home as it was believed to cause dreams too shocking for their sensibilities! Another suggestion was that inhaling the fragrance while visualising the way you want your body to look could help you lose weight. Honeysuckle hung on the door was believed to keep out fevers and the ill-intentioned. It could also protect against witches. Honeysuckle provides both food and shelter for dormice. They use its shredded bark to build their nests and eat the nectar-rich flowers.

**Japanese honeysuckle (*Lonicera japonica*)**

## References:

[Accessed 01.05.17]

1. B. Jensen; A Small Guide to Nature's Fragrances; http://www.bojensen.net/EssentialOilsEng/EssentialOils13A/EssentialOils13A.htm [Accessed 01.05.17]

2. Medical News Today, (28th March 2009); Widely Used Fragrance Ingredients In Shampoos And Conditioners Are Frequent Causes Of Eczema; http://www.medicalnewstoday.com/releases/144041.php [Accessed 01.05.17]

3. S. Cotton; Molecule of the Month, Linalool; http://www.chm.bris.ac.uk/motm/linalool/linaloolh.htm [Accessed 01.05.17]

4. American Chemical Society, (23rd July 2009); "Stop And Smell The Flowers – The Scent Really Can Soothe Stress."; ScienceDaily; www.sciencedaily.com/releases/2009/07/090722110901.htm [Accessed 01.05.17]

5. M. Colbert; Terpene Profile – Linalool; The Leaf Online; http://theleafonline.com/c/science/2014/09/terpene-profile-linalool/ [Accessed 01.05.17]

6. R. Ravizza, M.B. Gariboldi, R. Molteni, E. Monti, (2008); Linalool, a plant-derived monoterpene alcohol, reverses doxorubicin resistance in human breast adenocarcinoma cells; *Oncol. Rep.*, 20(3), 625–30; doi: 10.3892/or_00000051

7. S. Cotton; Molecule of the Month, Methyl Jasmonate; http://www.chm.bris.ac.uk/motm/jasmine/jasminec.htm

8. Y. Yukimune, H. Tabata, Y. Higashi, Y. Hara, (1996); Methyl jasmonate-induced overproduction of paclitaxel and baccatin III in *Taxus* cell suspension cultures; *Nat. Biotechnol.*, 14(9), 1129–32; doi: 10.1038/nbt0996-1129

9. D.-C. Ilieş, V. Rădulescu, L. Duţu, (2014); Volatile constituents from the flowers of two species of honeysuckle (*Lonicera japonica and Lonicera caprifolium*); *Farmacia*, 62(1), 194–201; http://www.revistafarmacia.ro/201401/art-17-ilies%20194-201.pdf [Accessed 24.09.17]

10. T. Røstelien, A.-K. Borg-Karlson, J. Fäldt, U. Jacobsson, H. Mustaparta, (2000); The Plant Sesquiterpene Germacrene D Specifically Activates a Major Type of Antennal Receptor Neuron of the Tobacco Budworm Moth *Heliothis virescens*; *Chem. Senses*, 25(2), 141–8; doi: 10.1093/chemse/25.2.141

11. K. Noge, J.X. Becerra, (2009); Germacrene D, A Common Sesquiterpene in the Genus *Bursera* (Burseraceae); *Molecules*, 14(2), 5289–97; doi: 10.3390/molecules14125289

12. G. James, G. Schultz, R. Wolcott, (2016); Wound biofilm consensus – Recommendations from an expert panel; *Wound Care Canada*, 14(3), 28–9; https://www.woundscanada.ca/docman/public/wound-care-canada-magazine/2016-14-no3/120-full-issue-3/file [Accessed 01.05.17]

13. M.L. Langford, A.L. Atkin, K.W. Nickerson, (2009); Cellular interactions of farnesol, a quorum-sensing molecule produced by *Candida albicans*; *Future Microbiol.*, 4(10), 1353–62; doi: 10.2217/fmb.09.98

14. Dr Mercola, (31st August 2015); Flowers Used in Chinese Herbal Medicine; http://articles.mercola.com/sites/articles/archive/2015/08/31/7-flowers-chinese-medicine.aspx#_edn3 [Accessed 01.05.17]

15. J. Tae, S.-W. Han, J.-Y. Yoo, J.-A Kim, O.-H. Kang, O.-S. Baek, J.-P. Lim, D.-K. Kim, Y.-H. Kim, K.-H. Bae, Y.-M. Lee, (2003); Anti-inflammatory effect of *Lonicera japonica* in proteinase-activated receptor 2-mediated paw edema; *Clin. Chim. Acta*, 330(1–2), 165–171; doi: 10.1016/S0009-8981(03)00017-2

16. Y.Q. Li, W. Yuan, S.L. Zhang, (1992); Clinical and experimental study of xiao er ke chuan ling oral liquid in the treatment of infantile bronchopneumonia; *Zhongguo Zhong Xi Yi Jie He Za Zhi*, 12(12), 719–21; PMID: 1304839

17. Z. Zhou, X. Li, J. Liu, L. Dong, Q. Chen, J. Liu, H. Kong, Q. Zhang, X. Qi, D. Hou, L. Zhang, G. Zhang, Y. Liu, Y. Zhang, J. Li, J. Wang, X. Chen, H. Wang, J. Zhang, H. Chen, K. Zen C.-Y. Zhang, (2015); Honeysuckle-encoded atypical microRNA2911 directly targets influenza A viruses; *Cell Res.*, 25(1), 39–49; doi: 10.1038/cr.2014.130

18. N. Anderson, (15th October 2014); Scientists Discover First 'Virological Penicillin'; SciNews; http://www.sci-news.com/medicine/science-virological-penicillin-honeysuckle-02206.html [Accessed 01.05.17]

# Wild Rose

## (*Rosa canina*)

*Rosa canina*, or dog rose, is usually found growing in hedgerows. The root was traditionally used to treat bites from rabid dogs and this may have led to its common name. Alternatively, it may be a corruption of 'dag rose', referring to the sharp thorns, like daggers. The thorns resemble the canine teeth of dogs so this may also account for the plant's name.

The fruits, known as rose hips, are a good source of vitamin C and other vitamins and flavonoids. They are actually false fruits formed from the stalk ends growing around the carpels and enclosing the small, hairy, 'real' fruits inside, each containing one seed.

According to data from the US Department of Agriculture, rose hips contain 426 mg of vitamin C/100 g fruit, compared to 32.5–71 for oranges or their juice (highest for raw oranges with peel) and 29.1 for limes.[1] During World War II, British schoolchildren gathered the hips and these were made into a syrup, used to ensure sufficient vitamin C was consumed by the population. Rose hip syrup is still taken today as a tonic to reduce tiredness and boost the body's defences against infections, particularly colds. Rose hips are also used to treat conditions of the bladder, gall-bladder and kidneys. The hairs around the seeds cause itching and ground rose hips are used in some commercial itching powders. They don't cause itching *via* an allergic reaction but act like wool fibres, stimulating the itch by a mechanical action.[2]

Vitamin C, or L-ascorbic acid, is needed in the body to protect cells and keep them healthy, to promote

**Wild Rose** is the Bach flower remedy for those who are apathetic.

wound-healing and to maintain healthy connective tissue. It is also an antioxidant which, in addition to its own activity, regenerates other antioxidants, including vitamin E. These antioxidant effects are of interest due to the role of oxidative stress in the development of cardiovascular disease and some cancers.[3] In the UK the recommended daily intake of vitamin C required by an adult is 40 mg. A lack of the vitamin can cause scurvy but the body can't store it and sufficient quantities are usually obtained from the diet.[4] However, some people advocate supplement doses of 1,000 mg or higher, although these can sometimes cause stomach problems.

Most famously, eminent chemist Linus Pauling published claims that high doses of vitamin C could prevent and treat the common cold and cancer.[5,6] The winner of two Nobel prizes, Pauling was also a leading peace campaigner and anti-nuclear activist. He coined the term orthomolecular medicine – meaning using the right molecules in the right amounts – to describe the method of treating patients with large doses of nutrients already found in the body. Although there was evidence of the efficacy of vitamin C, there was also contradictory evidence, some of which was allegedly misleading and designed to discredit Pauling.[7]

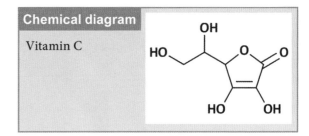

Chemical diagram

Vitamin C

Today, the position of the scientific establishment is that there is insufficient evidence to support the therapeutic use of high doses of vitamin C.[3] However, the benefit of supplementation with antioxidants has become more widely accepted.[8]

One source of inconsistency in studies on vitamin C is the method of administration. If taking it orally the blood plasma concentration can rise to 220 µM, however, intravenous injection of the vitamin can raise the level to 26,000 µM. At this level, vitamin C selectively targets tumour cells and may act as a pro-oxidant, promoting oxidation to produce the cytotoxic compound hydrogen peroxide. Another issue is that levels before and after supplementation are often unknown; when studying the effects of vitamin C on certain conditions, a patient with an already optimal vitamin C level would not be expected to experience any benefit from taking more.[3]

There is evidence to support some medicinal uses of rose hips, including to treat some of the symptoms of osteoarthritis. Powdered rose hips were found to reduce pain but larger-scale studies and a full safety evaluation of this treatment are still required.[9]

Hanging a rose over the dinner table traditionally symbolised that all confidences shared would be held sacred. This is the origin of the phrase *sub rosa*, meaning in confidence or in secret. Today, the plaster ornament at the centre of a ceiling is still known as a rose. There is an association between the Jacobites and the white rose, linked to the secrecy required by their cause.

Rose species produce a variety of flower colours from white to red. According to Mediterranean legend, the origin of white and red roses are the prayers of a falsely accused maiden, burned for her crime. Her prayers

**Rose hips**

quenched the flames and the charred brands became red roses while the unburnt ones became white roses. Dog rose flowers have five petals and are usually pale pink although white and darker pink flowers are also found.

While dog roses have only a faint scent, many species are scented and these are the source of rose essential oil or otto of roses (rose otto). Legend has it that this was discovered when, at the bridal feast of the princess Nour-Djihan and the Emperor Djihanguyr, the couple were rowing on a canal filled with rose water. The heat of the sun separated the oil from the water and it was skimmed off. The oil was found to have an exquisite perfume and by 1612 it was being traded by manufacturers in Iran.

Today, the oil comes mainly from damask roses (*Rosa x damascena*) or cabbage roses (*Rosa centifolia*) grown in Bulgaria, Turkey and France. It takes around 3 kg of rose petals to produce 1 ml of rose otto.[10] While this is made by steam distillation, rose absolute, commonly used in perfumery, is obtained by solvent extraction (using hexane or alcohol). Due to the higher yield obtained by solvent extraction, rose absolute is about three times cheaper.[10] The oil contains a large number of chemical compounds including citronellol, geraniol, rose oxide and β-ionone.[11] Citronellol is the major component of the oil (38%) and geraniol is also significant (14%).

However, the compound β-damascenone is the most important contributor to the fragrance (0.14% of the oil but 70% of the odour, based on the odour threshold for the human nose). β-Ionone is also significant (0.03% of the oil but 19.2% of the odour).[11] The quantity of β-damascenone in rose oil is a determinant of quality but its detection is a challenge due to the very small amounts present (less than 100 ppm). A high selectivity technique known as GC/MS/MS can be used. This is a combination of gas chromatography which separates the oil components and tandem mass spectrometry which analyses molecular fragments and compares the standard 'fingerprints' of chemical compounds with those from the sample.[12]

**Chemical diagram**

β-Damascenone

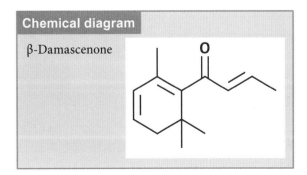

β-Damascenone is also present in red wine. Although it generally occurs below its odour detection limit in a wine matrix, it does influence the smell by enhancing the fruity notes of ethyl cinnamate and ethyl caproate and masking the herbaceous aroma of IBMP (3-isobutyl-2-methoxypyrazine).[13]

Rose oil is used in aromatherapy for stress and grief, to nurture the body and in cosmetics for mature skin. Due to the high cost it is sometimes adulterated with geraniol or other oils which are rich in geraniol such as palmarosa or geranium. Rose oil is used in perfumery, for example in J'Adore and Poison by Christian Dior.[11]

Damask rose was traditionally used to treat coughs, digestive problems, abdominal and chest pain and to staunch bleeding. Apothecary rose (*Rosa gallica* var. *officinalis*) has sedative and antidepressant properties, is an astringent and can lower cholesterol. Traditionally, petals were dried, rolled into beads and strung onto chains to form a rosary, for religious use. Flowers are used in pot pourri and the petals are sometimes used as confetti.

Wild roses attract rose gall wasps, *Diplolepis rosae*. Females lay their eggs in the unopened leaf buds. The rose responds by developing a gall known as a rose bedeguar gall, Robin's pincushion gall or moss gall. This resembles a ball of fluffy moss on the stem. The galls are sometimes invaded by inquilines like *Periclistus brandtii* wasps which live harmlessly within them.[14] Medicinally, the galls were used for their astringency and placed under the pillow at night to induce sleep.

**A rose bedeguar gall**

**References:**

1. USDA Food Composition Databases; https://ndb.nal.usda.gov/ [Accessed 04.05.17]

2. M.R. Albert, (1998); Novelty shop 'itching powder'; *Australas. J. Dermatol.*, 39(3), 188–9; doi: 10.1111/j.1440-0960.1998.tb01281.x

3. National Institutes of Health, Office of Dietary Supplements, (updated 11th February 2016); Vitamin C Fact Sheet for Health Professionals; https://ods.od.nih.gov/factsheets/VitaminC-HealthProfessional/#en78 [Accessed 04.05.17]

4. NHS Choices, (last reviewed 3rd March 2017); Vitamin C; http://www.nhs.uk/Conditions/vitamins-minerals/Pages/Vitamin-C.aspx [Accessed 04.05.17]

5. L. Pauling, (1970); Vitamin C and the Common Cold; W.H. Freeman, ISBN 0716701596

6. E. Cameron, L. Pauling, (1979); Cancer and Vitamin C: A Discussion of the Nature, Causes, Prevention, and Treatment of Cancer with Special Reference to the Value of Vitamin C; Linus Pauling Institute of Science and Medicine, ISBN 0393500004

7. W. Kehr, (update 14th June 2017); eBook: War between orthodox and alternative medicine, chapter 3: Case study of scientific corruption [Pauling and Cameron]; https://www.cancertutor.com/war_pauling/ [Accessed 27.09.17]

8. U.S. National Library of Medicine; Promoting Vitamin C; The Linus Pauling Papers; https://profiles.nlm.nih.gov/ps/retrieve/Narrative/MM/p-nid/57 [Accessed 05.05.17]

9. R. Christensen, E.M. Bartels, R.D. Altman, A. Astrup, H. Bliddal, (2008); Does the hip powder of *Rosa canina* (rosehip) reduce pain in osteoarthritis patients: a meta-analysis of randomized controlled trials; *Osteoarthritis Cartilage*, 16(9), 965–72; doi: 10.1016/j.joca.2008.03.001

10. N. Whitehead, (30th September 2014); Essential oil profiles: How to choose a rose oil; https://www.oshadhi.co.uk/blog/essential-oil-profiles-how-to-choose-a-rose-oil/ [Accessed 05.05.17]

11. J.C. Leffingwell; Rose (*Rosa damascena*); http://www.leffingwell.com/rose.htm [Accessed 05.05.17]

12. Agilent Technologies Inc.; GC/MS/MS analysis of β-damascenone in rose oil; https://www.agilent.com/cs/library/applications/A01697.pdf [Accessed 05.05.17]

13. B. Pineau, J.-C. Barbe, C. Van Leeuwen, D. Dubourdieu, (2007); Which Impact for β-Damascenone on Red Wines Aroma?; *J. Agric. Food Chem.*, 55(10), 4103–8; doi: 10.1021/jf070120r

14. R.Griffiths, (15th August 2014); Robin's Pincushion or Rose Bedeguar Galls on Wild Rose; https://www.youtube.com/watch?v=IZBqtm_ehcQ [Accessed 05.05.17]

# Mimulus

## (*Mimulus guttatus*)

The genus *Mimulus* formerly contained about 150 species sometimes known as monkey flowers or musk flowers, mainly native to North America and Australia. The name may have originated from the Latin *mimus*, for actor or mimic or the Ancient Greek *mimo* meaning monkey, due to the supposed resemblance of the flowers to a smiling monkey's face or to an actor's mask.[1] In 2012, a taxonomic reclassification of the genus was suggested based on molecular-phylogenetic and morpho-taxonomic studies. All the species discussed here were reclassified in genus *Erythranthe* and revised names are given[2] in parentheses, where the species are first mentioned.

*Mimulus guttatus* (*Erythranthe guttata*) is also known as the common yellow monkey flower or seep monkey flower. It is native to western North America, commonly found growing on the banks of seeps (small pools or springs). The species name comes from the Latin for spotted, referring to the red spots usually present on its yellow, tube-like flowers.

*Mimulus moschatus* (*Erythranthe moschata*), or musk flower, was the source of the fabled scent musk. Plants were sent back to Britain from North America by botanist and plant hunter David Douglas in 1826 and were popularly grown on windowsills for their scent. However, unscented plants eventually predominated and folklorists suggested the loss of scent was the plant's protest against the carnage of World War I.

Since the 1940s, the genus has been used as a model plant system in evolutionary and ecological genetics.[3]

**Mimulus** is the Bach flower remedy for those who are shy and timid or are afraid of a specific thing.

The genome of *Mimulus guttatus* has been sequenced and information on the genomes of *Mimulus lewisii* (*Erythranthe lewisii*) and *Mimulus cardinalis* (*Erythranthe cardinalis*) is also available. The genus shows great diversity and variation in traits such as habitat specialisation, floral divergence and the fertility of hybrids is observed, even within species.

With the genetic data available, the links between genes and observed traits can be studied. Recent work looked at the floral colours in 11 *Mimulus* species. These were found to originate from a mixture of up to five carotenoid pigments (related to carotenes) which help attract pollinators and also protect the plant by acting as antioxidants. Major components in *Mimulus guttatus* are the relatively rare pigments deepoxyneoxanthin* and mimulaxanthin. These are conjugated polyenes, having alternate single and double C–C bonds along part of the molecule and are also allenic, *i.e.* contain C=C=C linkages. Study of their biosynthesis and its genetic origin is on-going.[4]

The defence mechanisms of *Mimulus guttatus* show substantial variation. Even within a given plant, leaves of different ages contain different amounts of various phenylpropanoid glycosides (PPGs). These are compounds such as verbascoside (also found in vervain and discussed in the vervain section) and mimuloside, which act as chemical defences against most generalist herbivores. Quantities also vary within groups of plants growing together and between separate populations. This is partly dependent on the development of other defences such as trichomes (hairs).[5] However, in the case of one specialist insect, *Junonia coenia* (common buckeye caterpillar), verbascoside is found to act as a feeding stimulant rather than a deterrent.[6] PPGs show a wide

range of biological activities including antibacterial, antifungal and antioxidant effects and tumour-cell suppression.[5]

The method by which *Mimulus guttatus* plants guide pollinators has also been studied. While the flower petals appear yellow to the human eye, under ultraviolet (UV) light there are one of two types of nectar guides. These are termed runways, in which the entire lower petal absorbs UV light, or bulls-eyes, where UV absorption is limited to the upper portion of the lower petal near the corolla throat. The runway guide is dominant but in populations which are perennial (*i.e.* live for more than two years) bulls-eyes are usually found instead (and occasionally both occur). Nectar guides are significant because bees are found to avoid novel guides, preferring the familiar. As a result, populations where unusual forms predominate may find themselves unattractive to all but a few bees. Within a mixed population, bees show a degree of floral constancy, favouring one or the other guide-type.[7]

## Chemical diagram

Deepoxyneoxanthin

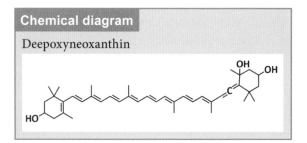

*Mimulus* species have also been studied in relation to their adaptation to copper in the environment, including a study of *Mimulus guttatus* growing around a disused copper mine in Copperopolis, California. The tolerance is due to the action of a single major gene along with some other genetic modifiers.[8]

Monkey flower plants provide a source of sodium chloride (salt) which they concentrate from the soil and so can be used as a salt substitute.[1] Leaves were eaten in salads or were occasionally cooked and have a slightly bitter taste, becoming more bitter with age. Cooking destroys the bitter compounds.[1]

One species, *Mimulus lewisii*, has glandular hairs on the leaves which trap insects. This plant belongs to a group of partially carnivorous plants, supplementing its sugar-based diet with insects.[1]

Medicinally, yellow monkey flower is astringent so can be used to staunch bleeding and promote healing of wounds. A poultice made from the leaves was sometimes used by Native Americans to treat wounds and rope burns. A decoction of the leaves and stems was used in a herbal steam bath for chest and back

soreness.[9,10] Today, the plant is taken as an antidepressant especially in cases of paranoia, phobias, oversensitivity and fear and to treat nerve pain such as sciatica. It can also be used in a poultice and a combination with milky oats is suggested to treat 'crispy critterness'![11]

### References:

1. A. Leuchtmann, D. Schmidt, L.P. Bush, (2000); http://www.softschools.com/facts/plants/monkey_flowers_facts/1560/ [Accessed 06.05.17]

2. W.R. Barker, G.L. Nesom, P.M. Beardsley, N.S. Fraga, (2012); A taxonomic conspectus of Phrymaceae: A narrowed circumscriptions for *Mimulus*, new and resurrected genera, and new names and combinations; *Phytoneuron*, 2012-39, 1–60; http://www.phytoneuron.net/PhytoN-Phrymaceae.pdf [Accessed 05.05.17]

3. http://www.mimulusevolution.org/background.php [Accessed 06.05.17]

4. A.M. LaFountain, H.A. Frank, Y.-W. Yuan, (2015); Carotenoid composition of the flowers of *Mimulus lewisii* and related species: Implications regarding the prevalence and origin of two unique, allenic pigments; *Arch. Biochem. Biophys.*, 573, 32–9; doi: 10.1016/j.abb.2015.03.006

*Mimulus lewisii*

5. K. Keefover-Ring, L.M. Holeski, M.D. Bowers, A.D. Clauss, R.L. Lindroth, (2014); Phenylpropanoid glycosides of *Mimulus guttatus* (yellow monkeyflower); *Phytochem. Lett.*, 10, 132–9; doi: 10.1016/j.phytol.2014.08.016

6. L.M. Holeski , K. Keefover-Ring, M.D. Bowers, Z.T. Harnenz, R.L. Lindroth, (2013); Patterns of Phytochemical Variation in *Mimulus guttatus* (Yellow Monkeyflower); *J. Chem. Ecol.*, 39(4), 525–36; doi: 10.1007/s10886-013-0270-7

7. M.L. Peterson, T.J. Miller, K.M. Kay, (2015); An ultraviolet floral polymorphism associated with life history drives pollinator discrimination in *Mimulus guttatus*; *Am. J. Bot.*, 102(3), 396–406; doi: 10.3732/ajb.1400415

8. M.R. MacNair, S.E. Smith, Q.J. Cumbes, (1993); Heritability and distribution of variation in degree of copper tolerance in *Mimulus guttatus* at Copperopolis, California; *Heredity*, 71(5), 445–55; doi: 10.1038/hdy.1993.162

9. http://www.pfaf.org/user/Plant.aspx?LatinName= Mimulus+guttatus [Accessed 06.05.17]

10. Yellow monkeyflower; http://montana.plant-life.org/ index.html [Accessed 29.09.17]

11. K. Rose, (10ᵗʰ March 2008); The Magic of Monkeyflowers; http://bearmedicineherbals.com/the-magic-of-monkeyflowers.html [Accessed 06.05.17]

* Deepoxyneoxanthin is sometimes shown with a single C–C bond instead of a double bond in the ring on the left-hand side of the diagram as drawn (*e.g.* in PubChem). However, the version shown here is more common and is consistent with the molecular weight given in reference 4.

# Impatiens

*(Impatiens glandulifera)*

*Impatiens glandulifera* originates in the Himalayan Mountains and is known as Himalayan balsam, kiss-me-on-the-mountain, Indian balsam or jewel weed. It has large, usually pink, hat-like flowers, reflected in several of its other common names including policeman's helmet, gnome's hatstand and bobby tops. Their scent divides opinion; it is described either as like disinfectant or like peaches. Flowers are pollinated by bees which can be seen disappearing deep inside, coming out covered in pollen except for their rear end; this is alluded to in another common name, bee bums![1] The species is part of the same genus as the common busy Lizzie (*Impatiens walleriana*).

The genus name *Impatiens* alludes to their method of seed dispersal. Ripe seed pods open explosively and shoot their seeds up to seven metres. Each plant can produce about 2500 seeds.[2] Other common names for the plants are touch-me-not, quick-in-the-hand or stinky pops, all relating to the effect of touch on the pods. The species *glandulifera* was introduced to the UK in 1839 and became popular in Victorian gardens. Its large size (2–3 metres) and lanceolate leaves up to 40 cm long appealed to gardeners of the time (like other plants introduced by the Victorians such as Japanese knotweed and giant hogweed). It was affordable to all, unlike the expensive orchids the Victorian rich grew in their greenhouses, and the species was sometimes known as poor man's orchids.[1]

Within 10 years of introduction it had escaped the confines of gardens and spread along waterways, its energetic seed dispersal and the ability of the seeds to

**Impatiens** is the Bach flower remedy for agitation and impatience.

Impatiens   133

float facilitating rapid colonisation. It is considered to be a weed by some, growing abundantly by rivers and on waste ground, shading and crowding out native plants. This can also have an impact on native invertebrate populations, mainly those which live above ground, which has a knock-on effect on the whole ecosystem.[3] As it dies back during the winter months, Himalayan balsam leaves river banks exposed, speeding up erosion. It is actively removed by so-called balsam bashers, groups of conservationists who view it as a threat to native species and who cut down the plants and compost them.[1] However, its removal can also lead to soil erosion and there are no guarantees which, if any, plants will recolonise the balsam-free ground – one so-called invasive weed may be replaced by another.

Recently, biological control has been trialled using Himalayan balsam rust fungus.[4] While Himalayan balsam has no natural predators in the UK, the fungus maintains control over its spread in Central Asia, where it is native. The fungus, *Puccinia komarovii* var. *glanduliferae*, affects the plants both at the seedling stage, reducing survival and by retarding photosynthesis in the leaves of mature plants, limiting seed production. Results from 2016 suggested that there was a large genetic variation within the Himalayan balsam growing in the test area and this made susceptibility to the rust fungus strain used

**Exploded seed pod and seeds**

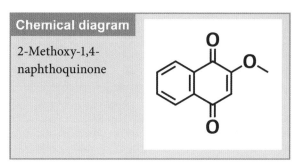

variable. Tests on other strains of the fungus and with different release strategies are now underway.[5]

Another factor involved in the perceived invasiveness of Himalayan balsam is that it contains allelopathic compounds which are leached into the soil and inhibit germination of other plants nearby. One of these is 2-methoxy-1,4-naphthoquinone which is released by the roots and leached from the leaves by rain.[6] It is also found in garden balsam (*Impatiens balsamina*). Medicinally, this compound has shown antifungal[7] and antibacterial[8,9] activities and is active against some types of cancer cells.[10]

The related compound lawsone (2-hydroxy-1,4-naphthoquinone) is a red-orange dye also found in this species and in henna (*Lawsonia inermis*) and garden balsam. Henna has been used as a skin and hair dye for over 6,000 years. When lawsone is released it binds to the protein molecule keratin in the skin or hair, creating a fast stain which persists until the skin or hair is shed.[11] Lawsone is similar to juglone (5-hydroxy-1,4-naphthoquinone) which occurs in walnut trees and is also used as a dye (see walnut section).

Himalayan balsam flowers contain numerous flavonoids including astragalin and ampelopsin (dihydromyricetin).[12] The latter compound is a major active component in Rattan tea, made from the leaves of *Ampelopsis grossedentata* (commonly known as moyeam) and used in traditional Chinese medicine. It has been credited with most of the beneficial properties of the tea including the antibacterial, anti-inflammatory and antitumour effects and its action as a liver protector and regulator of blood glucose and lipids.[13] Ampelopsin has been found to be a promising treatment for alcohol-use disorders, counteracting acute ethanol intoxication and symptoms associated with ethanol use or withdrawal. It may be a key contributor to the effects of the plant *Hovenia dulcis* (Japanese raisin tree) as a hangover cure.[14]

In areas where it is native, Himalayan balsam is used medicinally. The roots and leaves are crushed and applied to the forehead, hands and feet to provide a cooling effect. A decoction of the leaves is used to treat stress and mental tension and the flowers to treat snake bites.[15] The young leaves and shoots can be cooked and eaten in small quantities. Seeds can be eaten raw or toasted and ground to make flour. Crushed, they can be used as a spice or substituted in any recipe that calls for hazelnuts. In parts of India they are sometimes added to stews and curries. Green seedpods can be eaten like mangetout and flowers used to make floral jams.[2]

**Henna tattoo**

**References:**

1. R. Mabey, (24th June 2011); Indian Balsam; Mabey in the Wild, Series 1 Episode 4; http://www.bbc.co.uk/programmes/b012qnl4#synopsis [Accessed 07.05.17]

2. Changing Lifestyle Blog, (16th February 2015); Weed of the Week *Impatiens glandulifera* Himalayan Balsam; https://changinglifestyleblog.wordpress.com/2015/02/ [Accessed 07.05.17]

3. R.A. Tanner, S. Varia, R. Eschen, S. Wood, S.T. Murphy, A.C. Gange, (2013); Impacts of an Invasive Non-Native Annual Weed, *Impatiens glandulifera*, on Above- and Below-Ground Invertebrate Communities in the United Kingdom; *PLoS ONE*, 8(6), e67271; doi: 10.1371/journal.pone.0067271

4. Centre for Agriculture and Biosciences International; https://himalayanbalsam.cabi.org/ [Accessed 07.05.17]

5. S. Varia, K. Pollard, C. Ellison, (2016); Implementing a Novel Weed Management Approach for Himalayan Balsam: Progress on Biological Control in the UK; *Outlooks on Pest Management*, 27(5), 198–203; doi: 10.1564/v27_oct_02 [Accessed 07.05.17]

6. R. Ruckli, K. Hesse, G. Glauser, H.-P. Rusterholz, B.Baur, (2014); Inhibitory Potential of Naphthoquinones Leached from Leaves and Exuded from Roots of the Invasive Plant *Impatiens glandulifera*; *J. Chem. Ecol.*, 40(4), 371–8; doi: 10.1007/s10886-014-0421-5

7. J.E. Little, T.J. Sproston, M.W. Foote, (1948); Isolation and anti-fungal action of naturally occurring 2-methoxy-1,4-naphthoquinone; *J.Biol. Chem.*, 174, 335–42; http://www.jbc.org/content/174/1/335.full.pdf [Accessed 07.05.17]

8. X. Yang, D.K. Summerhurst, S.F. Koval, C. Ficker, M.L. Smith, M.A. Bernards, (2001); Isolation of an antimicrobial compound from *Impatiens balsamina* L. using bioassay-guided fractionation; *Phytother. Res.*, 15(8), 676–80; doi: 10.1002/ptr.906

9. Y.-C. Wang, W.-Y. Li, D.-C. Wu, J.-J. Wang, C.-H. Wu, J.-J. Liao, C.-K. Lin, (2011); In Vitro Activity of 2-methoxy-1,4-naphthoquinone and Stigmasta-7,22-diene-3β-ol from *Impatiens balsamina* L. against Multiple Antibiotic-Resistant *Helicobacter pylori*; *Evid. Based Complement. Alternat. Med.*, vol. 2011, Article ID 704721, 8 pages; doi: 10.1093/ecam/nep147

10. Z.-S. Ding, F.-S. Jiang, N.-P. Chen, G.-Y. Lv, C.-G. Zhu, (2008); Isolation and Identification of an Anti-tumor Component from Leaves of *Impatiens balsamina*; *Molecules*, 13(2), 220–9; doi: 10.3390/molecules13020220

11. https://hennacolorlab.com/what-is-henna/ [Accessed 07.05.17]

12. M.N. Vieira, P. Winterhalter, G. Jerz, (2016); Flavonoids from the flowers of *Impatiens glandulifera* Royle isolated by high performance countercurrent chromatography; *Phytochem. Anal.*, 27(2), 116–25; doi: 10.1002/pca.2606

13. X. Kou, N. Chen, (2012); Pharmacological potential of ampelopsin in Rattan tea; *Food Science and Human Wellness*, 1(1), 14–8; doi: 10.1016/j.fshw.2012.08.001

14. Y. Shen, A.K. Lindemeyer, C. Gonzalez, X.M. Shao, I. Spigelman, R.W. Olsen, J. Liang, (2012); Dihydromyricetin as a Novel Anti-Alcohol Intoxication Medication; *J. Neurosci.*, 32(1), 390–401; doi: 10.1523/JNEUROSCI.4639-11.2012

15. M. Kumar, Y. Paul, V. K. Anand, (2009); An Ethnobotanical Study of Medicinal Plants used by the Locals in Kishtwar, Jammu and Kashmir, India; *Ethnobotanical Leaflets*, 13(10), 1240–56; http://opensiuc.lib.siu.edu/cgi/viewcontent.cgi?article=1635&context=ebl [Accessed 07.05.17]

# Cerato

*(Ceratostigma willmottianum)*

Better known as Chinese plumbago, *Ceratostigma willmottianum* is native to China and Tibet. Plants in two genera of the family Plumbaginaceae, *Plumbago* and *Ceratostigma*, are sometimes referred to as plumbagos or leadworts (*plumbum* is Latin for lead). These names may be related to the use of the plants by Pliny the Elder and others to treat lead poisoning or to the lead-blue colour of the flowers.[1] The genus name *Ceratostigma* comes from the Greek *keras*, for horn, referring to the horn-shaped appearance of the stigma (in the flower, the stigma is the head of the pistil where pollen is deposited and begins fertilisation). Species *willmottianum* has purple-edged, diamond-shaped leaves which turn red in the autumn.

The species is named in honour of horticulturalist Ellen Willmott (1858–1934) who sponsored the plant-hunting expedition on which it was discovered by Ernest H. Wilson.[2] She is also remembered for scattering seeds of giant sea holly, *Eryngium giganteum*, whenever she visited a garden and this species is known as Miss Willmott's ghost.[2] She was one of the first woman to be elected to the Linnaean Society but, although she worked in her own garden, she didn't rate female gardeners and wrote that young women were 'utterly hopeless and unsafe in the borders'.[3] Her extravagant spending eventually left her penniless and she suffered ignominy when she was wrongly accused of shoplifting. All that is left today of her once-great garden, Warley Place in Essex, are a few of her plants and the overgrown daffodil fields, which were once booby-trapped to repel plant thieves. The site is now a

**Cerato** is the Bach flower remedy for those who don't trust their own judgement.

**Miss Willmott's ghost (*Eryngium giganteum*)**

nature reserve managed by Essex Wildlife Trust.[3]

Chinese plumbago is used in folk medicine to treat rheumatism, traumatic injury and parotitis[4] (inflammation of the parotid glands, large salivary glands in front of the ears; mumps is infectious, viral parotitis). Analysis of the chemical compounds present in extracts of the whole plant showed the presence of *N-trans*-caffeoyltyramine, aesculetin, plumbagin, plumbolactones A and B, plumbagic acid and nine other compounds.[4]

*N-trans*-caffeoyltyramine is an antioxidant[5] and has anti-inflammatory effects.[6] It inhibits the bacterium *Helicobacter pylori*, a causative factor of gastrointestinal illnesses such as peptic ulcers and gastritis which also increases the risk of stomach cancer.[7]

Aesculetin (6,7-dihydroxycoumarin) is also an antioxidant and is active against a range of human cancer cells including leukaemia and malignant melanoma.[8] It is also present in chicory. Aesculin, found in horse chestnuts, is the glucoside of aesculetin (formed by replacing one H atom with a glucose group; see horse

Plumbagin

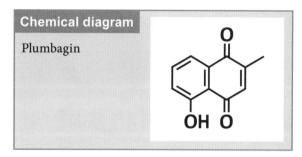

chestnut section for more information on one use of their interconversion).

Plumbagin is a yellow dye and medicinally has shown antimicrobial,[9] antifungal,[10] antimalarial,[11] anti-inflammatory, analgesic[12] and anticancer effects.[13] It is a bitter principle also found in *Plumbago europaea*. This plant has the common name dentallaria related to its use to relieve toothache. The acrid root promotes free flow of saliva when chewed and a decoction in olive oil has also been used to treat itching.

There are eight members of the genus *Ceratostigma*, including *Ceratostigma plumbaginoides*, or dwarf plumbago, which grows to only 50 cm tall, about half as tall as Chinese plumbago. The medicinal effects of this species have been studied and include antimicrobial and antioxidant properties.[14]

The vivid blue colour of the flowers of leadworts is uncommon; less than 10% of flowers are blue. There is no truly blue pigment in nature and the colour is produced in the flowers by modification of red anthocyanin pigments. The rarity of blue orchid flowers has led some plant breeders to dye white flowers blue.[15]

## References:

1.  G. Klingaman, (9th November 2012); Plant of the Week Plumbago or Leadwort; https://www.uaex.edu/yard-garden/resource-library/plant-week/plumbago-11-9-12.aspx [Accessed 09.05.17]

2.  Oxonian Gardener, (2nd October 2012); Ellen Willmott: Gardener and Plantswoman; www.oxoniangardener.co.uk/ellen-ann-willmott-8446/ [Accessed 08.05.17]

3.  S. Gordon; Ellen Ann Willmott - a true genius of the place; Parks & Gardens UK; http://www.parksandgardens.org/learning/topics/176-historical-profiles/493-ellen-ann-willmott-a-true-genius-of-the-place?showall=1&limitstart= [Accessed 08.05.17]

4.  J.-M. Yue, J. Xu, Y. Zhao, H.-D. Sun, Z.-W. Lin, (1997); Chemical Components from *Ceratostigma willmottianum*; *J. Nat. Prod.*, 60(10), 1031–3; doi: 10.1021/np970044u

5.  A.M. Al-Taweel, S. Perveen, A.M. El-Shafae, G.A. Fawzy, A. Malik, N. Afza, L. Iqbal, M. Latif, (2012); Bioactive Phenolic Amides from *Celtis africana*; *Molecules*, 17(3), 2675–82; doi: 10.3390/molecules17032675

6.  H. Ko, E. Ahn, J.S. Oh, (2015); *N-trans*-caffeoyl tyramine isolated from *Tribulus terrestris* exerts antiinflammatory effects in lipopolysaccharide stimulated RAW 264.7 cells; *Int. J. Mol. Med.*, 36(4), 1042–8; doi: 10.3892/ijmm.2015.2301

7.  J. Cai, C. Han, T. Hu, J. Zhang, D. Wu, F. Wang, Y. Liu, J. Ding, K. Chen, J. Yue, X. Shen, H. Jiang, (2006); Peptide deformylase is a potential target for anti-*Helicobacter pylori* drugs: Reverse docking, enzymatic assay, and X-ray crystallography validation; *Protein Sci.*, 15(9), 2071–81; doi: 10.1110/ps.062238406

8.  C. Liang, W. Ju, S. Pei, Y. Tang, Y. Xiao, (2017); Pharmacological Activities and Synthesis of Esculetin and Its Derivatives: A Mini-Review; *Molecules*, 22(3), 387; doi: 10.3390/molecules22030387

9.  R. Jeyachandran, A. Mahesh, L. Cindrella, S. Sudhakar, K. Pazhanichamy, (2009); Antibacterial activity of plumbagin and root extracts of *Plumbago zeylanica* L.; *Acta Biol. Cracov. Bot.*, 51(1), 17–22; http://www2.ib.uj.edu.pl/abc/pdf/51_1/17_22_jeyachandran.pdf [Accessed 09.05.17]

10. M. Masuko, H. Egawa, A. Ueyama, K. Koshimizu, K. Kobata, J. Fumo, (1970); Plumbagin, an Antifungal Factor in *Ceratostigma willmottianum* (Plumbaginaceae Plant); *Ann. Phytopath. Soc. Japan*, 36(4), 286–8; doi: 10.3186/jjphytopath.36.286

11. W. Sumsakul, T. Plengsuriyakarn, K. Na-Bangchang, (2016); Pharmacokinetics, toxicity, and cytochrome P450 modulatory activity of plumbagin; *BMC Pharmacol. Toxicol.*, 17, 50; doi: 10.1186/s40360-016-0094-5

12. P. Luo, Y.F. Wong, L. Ge, Z.F. Zhang, Y. Liu, L. Liu, H. Zhou, (2010); Anti-inflammatory and Analgesic Effect of Plumbagin through Inhibition of Nuclear Factor-κB Activation; *J. Pharm. Exp. Ther.*, 335(3), 735–42; doi: 10.1124/jpet.110.170852

13. Y. Liu, Y. Cai, C. He, M. Chen, H. Li, (2017); Anticancer Properties and Pharmaceutical Applications of Plumbagin: A Review; *Am. J. Chin. Med.*, 45(3), 423–42; doi: 10.1142/S0192415X17500264

14. H.O. Elansary, K. Yessoufou, E.A. Mahmoud, K. Skalicka-Woźniak, (2016); *In vitro* Antioxidant and Antimicrobial Effects of *Ceratostigma plumbaginoides*; *Nat. Prod. Commun.*, 11(10), 1455–8; http://www.naturalproduct.us/JournalArchive.asp [Accessed 09.05.17]

15. T. Oder, (27th July 2017); The science of blue flowers; http://www.mnn.com/your-home/organic-farming-gardening/stories/the-science-of-blue-flowers [Accessed 04.10.17]

# Scleranthus

*(Scleranthus annuus)*

*Scleranthus annuus* is part of the carnation or Caryophyllaceae family[1] and is known by the common names German knotweed, German knotgrass, German moss or (annual) knawel. Knawel comes from the 16th century German *Knauel* for knotweed (literally, ball of yarn).[2,3] An alternative explanation was provided by Carl Linnaeus when teaching students at the University of Uppsala.

'Tragus, who was Professor in Leipzig, asked, when he should say the name of this, a Swedish student, who was not a botanist. He answered: "Knäfvelen" knows, which the Professor accepted and gave the herb the name of Knävel. The Dutch, who should print this, left the dots over ä and then it become Knavel.'[sic][4]

Native to Europe, Asia and North Africa, it is considered to be a weed elsewhere. It is low-growing, forming dense mats and has inconspicuous green flowers. The flowers have no petals and are made up of five sepals which spread outwards when in fruit. The genus name means hard flower, referring to the hardened, fruiting, outer parts of the flower.[5] In the UK, intensive arable farming with increased use of broad-spectrum herbicides has led to its decline and it is regarded as endangered in the wild.[1]

Knawel is astringent and diuretic. The vapour from pouring boiling water onto the herb was used as a cure for toothache[5] and a water decoction of the aerial parts was a treatment for visceral prolapse (where the internal organs have descended within the abdomen).[6]

Perennial knawel (*Scleranthus perennis*) is a host plant

**Scleranthus** is the Bach flower remedy for those who are indecisive.

for Polish cochineal bugs (*Porphyrophora polonica*).[7,8] Polish cochineal dyes were developed by the ancient Slavs and provided an economically important trade in Europe until the mid-16th century when the cheaper cochineal we know today was introduced (sometimes known as Mexican or American cochineal and made from *Dactylopius coccus*, hosted by prickly pears (*Opuntia* spp.)). The dye was used to colour textiles and in Poland as a colourant for some vodkas and an ingredient in folk medicines. The Turks sometimes used it to colour their horses' tails.[8]

The female bugs lay eggs in the ground and the larvae feed on the low-growing host plants, initially on the leaves but then on the roots, where they form protective cysts. Female larvae are harvested before they reach maturity; the plant is uprooted and each one yields approximately 10 insects. Harvest occurs in late June, around the time of St. John the Baptist's Day (June 24th) and the resulting dye is sometimes known as Saint John's blood. The larvae are killed using vinegar or boiling water and dried.[8]

The red dye arises from a chemical compound produced by the larvae for protection called carminic acid. This acid deters predators such as ants, although some other insects are immune. For example, the carnivorous caterpillar of one pyralid moth (*Laetilia coccidivora*) eats Mexican cochineal bugs and uses the carminic acid it ingests for its own defence.[9] Carminic acid makes up approximately 0.6% of the body weight of dried Polish cochineal bugs. This is much less than the quantity in Mexican bugs (15–25%).[10] The relatively high fat content of Polish bugs (about 30%) is problematic when dyeing textiles.[11]

## Chemical diagram

Carminic acid

Portrait of Polish military commander, Stefan Czarniecki (1599–1665), in a crimson costume typical of Polish magnates (dyed with Polish cochineal) by Brodero Matthisen

Harvest of the insects is labour-intensive and the plants are dug up so have to be replaced. To meet commercial demand when use of the dye was widespread, knawel was grown in plantations. Along with the much-reduced yield of carminic acid from Polish cochineal larvae, this accounts for the relative expense of the dye. In the 18th century, it began to be exported again to Russia and Central Asia but today, use of the dye is rare and in some places, *e.g.* the Ukraine, the insect is considered endangered.[8]

The legacy of the use of Polish cochineal can be seen in Slavic languages, where the words for red and June (or July) derive from the word for worm. In Polish for example, the three words are *czerwony*, *czerwiec* and *czerw*, respectively.[12]

Prostrate perennial knawel (*Scleranthus perennis* subsp. *prostratus*) is considered endangered in the UK and is one of 20 species included in the 'Back from the Brink' conservation initiative. This project was

*Scleranthus biflorus*

awarded £4.6 million National Lottery funding in 2017 and aims to help save some of the rarest species in England.[13]

*Scleranthus biflorus* is native to New Zealand and parts of Australia, where it is known as cushion bush, Canberra grass or lime lava.[14] It resembles moss and is used to provide green ground cover in dry areas where growing grass is difficult. As a result, it is sometimes termed 'Australian astroturf'.[15] An ointment was made by drying the plant, grinding it up and mixing the powder into a paste with oil from the New Zealand passion flower (*Passiflora tetrandra*). This was used by the Maoris to ease itching.[16]

**References:**

1. http://www.missouriplants.com/Greenopp/Scleranthus_annuus_page.html [Accessed 11.05.17]

2. http://www.dictionary.com/browse/knawel [Accessed 11.05.17]

3. http://www.plantlife.org.uk/uk/discover-wild-plants-nature/plant-fungi-species/annual-knawel [Accessed 10.05.17]

4. http://www2.nrm.se/fbo/hist/linnaeus/linnaeus.html.en [Accessed 10.05.17]

5. R. Hogg, G.W. Johnson, (1866); The Wild Flowers of Great Britain. Botanically and Popularly Described with Copious Notices of their History and Uses, Volume 3, Journal of Horticulture and Cottage Gardener Office, London, p 232; available at books.google.co.uk

6. T.L. Egoshina, E.A. Luginina, (2006); Medicinal plants in folk medicine of taiga zone of Russia: peculiarities of use and resources; in Plant, fungal and habitat diversity investigation and conservation. Proceedings of IV Balkan Botanical Congress – Sofia 20–26 June 2006, Ed. D. Ivanova, ISBN 978-954-9746-14-3, pp 624–31

7. Dr. Wolfe, (1764); An Account of the Polish Cochineal: In a Letter to Mr. Henry Baker, F.R.S. from Dr. Wolfe, of Warsaw; *Philosophical Transactions (1683-1775)*, 54, 91–8; www.jstor.org/stable/105531 [Accessed 11.05.17]

8. Antique Rugs of the Future Project; Insect Dyes; http://www.azerbaijanrugs.com/arfp-natural_dyes_insect_dyes.htm [Accessed 10.05.17]

9. T. Eisner, S. Nowicki, M. Goetz, J. Meinwald, (30th May 1980); Red Cochineal Dye (Carminic Acid): Its Role in Nature; *Science*, 208(4447), 1039–42; doi: 10.1126/science.208.4447.1039

10. T. Bechtold, R. Mussak, (2009); Handbook of Natural Colourants, John Wiley and Sons, ISBN 978-0-470-511992, p 7

11. B. Łagowska, K. Golan, (2009); Scale insects/Hemiptera, Coccoidea/ as a source of natural dye and other useful substances; *Aphids and Other Hemipterous Insects*, 15, 151–67; https://www.kul.pl/files/658/aphids15/11lagowskagolan.pdf [Accessed 11.05.17]

12. http://www.pysanky.info/Natural_Dyes/Insect_Dyes.html [Accessed 10.05.17]

13. The Guardian, (31st March 2017); Funding boost to help save England's rarest species from extinction; https://www.theguardian.com/environment/2017/mar/31/funding-boost-to-help-save-englands-rarest-species-from-extinction [Accessed 10.05.17]

14. Cris, (13th January 2015); Lime Lava; http://tenrandomfacts.com/lime-lava/ [Accessed 10.05.17]

15. Annie's Annuals and Perennials; *Scleranthus biflorus* "Australian Astroturf"; https://www.anniesannuals.com/plants/view/?id=2994 [Accessed 10.05.17]

16. R. Tipa, (23rd December 2015); He Aitaka a Tāne A handsome climber; Te Karaka; http://ngaitahu.iwi.nz/our_stories/he-aitaka-a-tanea-handsome-climber/ [Accessed 10.05.17]

Rock Rose is the Bach flower remedy for those suffering from terror.

# Rock Rose

## (Helianthemum nummularium)

The genus name comes from the Greek *helios* meaning sun and *anthemon* meaning flower. The species name relates to the coin-shaped flowers.[1] In the wild, flowers of *Helianthemum nummularium*, or common rockrose, are yellow although cultivated varieties can range from white to deep red. The species is sometimes known as flower of the sun or, in parts of Scotland, as solflower.[2] In the southeast of England it grows in chalky or limestone-rich soils which are alkaline but in Scotland it grows in much more acidic soils.

The species is an evergreen, bearing green leaves all year round. It can adapt to hot, dry conditions; the hotter the weather, the more dwarf it becomes. Although small in stature (usually 10–20 cm high), its roots can reach down to 50 cm making the plants very efficient at taking in water. Leaves are curled back at the edges and have densely hairy undersides, both of which reduce water loss. In extreme heat the plant sheds some of its leaves to reduce the surface area for water evaporation.[3]

Although some of its common names suggest it is a sun-loving plant and the plant only opens its flowers in fine weather, it always directs them away from the sun. Only one opens at a time per inflorescence and each lasts for one day. Under the five petals there are five sepals but these are not equally sized – three are larger and usually striped and the other two are much smaller and narrower. The flower doesn't produce nectar but it is pollinated by insects. The stamens are sensitive to movement and dampness. As an insect brushes the anther, the stamens drop pollen onto its fur and turn to the side. This inflection makes it easier for the pistil, in the middle of the flower, to touch the next insect visitor so improving the chances of receiving pollen from a neighbouring flower on its stigma.[3]

The genus is part of the rock rose family (Cistaceae) and contains some plants known as frostweeds. The name frostweed is used for several plants including *Helianthemum canadense* (Canada frostweed or longbranch frostweed), *Verbesina virginica* (white crownbeard) and *Helianthemum bicknellii* (hoary frostweed) due to their ability to produce so-called frost flowers. These occur when water exuding from the stems freezes and curls into shapes which can resemble flowers.[4,5]

Frost flowers are rare as their formation requires a specific set of conditions; the air temperature must be below zero but the ground must not be frozen. The sap within the plant expands as it freezes causing long, thin cracks to form along the length of the stem. Water is drawn through the cracks by capillary action and freezes as it comes into contact with the air. As more water is drawn through it pushes the thin ice layers further from the stems causing a 'petal' to form. When the sun causes the air temperature to rise, the frost flowers quickly disappear.[6]

The genus *Helianthemum* contains over a hundred species and subspecies some of which are used medicinally. However, testing of the extracts from 11 different species showed significant differences in their

**Frost flowers**

**Underside of flower showing sepals**

chemical composition and this could be related to the medicinal properties. For example, the polyphenols identified in the leaves of some species (*e.g. Helianthemum alypoides*) were mainly tannins like gallic acid and egallic acid derivatives while others (*e.g. Helianthemum syriacum*) contained primarily flavonoids. Those containing most polyphenols were the strongest antioxidants and had the strongest antimicrobial effects.[7]

*Helianthemum canadense* was traditionally used to treat secondary syphilis, as an astringent, alterative and tonic and to treat scrofula (swelling of the lymph nodes in the neck caused by tuberculosis). An oil obtained from the plant was used as a treatment for cancer.

Another genus in the rock rose family is *Cistus* and an important resin, known as labdanum (sometimes ladanum), is obtained from two species, *Cistus creticus* (Cretan rockrose) and *Cistus ladanifer* (common gum cistus or crimson-spot rockrose). Their leaves are covered in glandular hairs which produce the resin. Goats and sheep eating the plants become covered in the resin and this was collected and sold.[8] Medicinally, it was used as a stimulant expectorant and emmenagogue (to promote menstruation), to treat catarrh and dysentery and in plasters.

The resin is still used today in perfumery although now it is obtained directly from the plants by treating with hot alkaline solution, followed by steam distillation to produce the oil in about 2% yield.[8] The scent resembles incense and ambergris and labdanum is sometimes used as an alternative to ambergris.

Ambergris (or ambra) is a pathological metabolite of the male sperm whale, probably produced due to injuries to its intestines resulting from eating certain foods like squid which have pointed beaks.[9,10] The whales produce a fatty substance to protect their intestines. When this is excreted from their body it floats on the surface of the sea where it is exposed to air, salt and sunlight and forms the grey, hard material with the characteristic sweet, earthy aroma of aged ambergris. Sometimes squid beaks can still be seen embedded.[10]

Ambergris has been prized since antiquity as a fixative in perfumery and also used medicinally to increase strength and virility and combat heart and brain ailments. It was even used as a flavouring to add spice to food and drink. It behaves as a fixative by binding to other odour molecules and extending the time before they are released.[10] The main component of fresh ambergris is the odourless ambrein which is a precursor of the scent compounds which include ambrox (ambroxan or ambroxide). Today, ambrox is usually synthesised from sclareol, obtained from

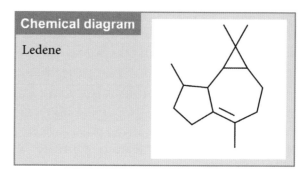

**Chemical diagram**

Ledene

clary sage (*Salvia sclarea*); sclareol is also found Cretan rockrose (see below). Ambrein has been found to increase male sexual behaviour, so may be behind the traditional use of ambergris as an aphrodisiac.[11] Although colloquially termed whale vomit, ambergris is probably excreted from the other end of the body! As sperm whales are endangered, the use of ambergris is controversial and secrecy sometimes surrounds it. However, it is rumoured to be an ingredient of well-known perfumes such as Chanel Number 5. And not for nothing is it known as gold of the sea – pieces washed up on beaches can be sold for about $20 per gram.[12]

Labdanum oil contains over 300 constituents, the most abundant of which (about 9%) is ledene[9] (also known as viridiflorene). Ledene has a potential use along with other compounds in the treatment of ocular demodex (eye lash mites).[13] Other components of the oil include ambrox, α-ambrinol and 2,2,6-trimethyl-2-cyclohexanone, which are all used in perfumery and/or as flavourings.[9]

Examples of a class of chemical compounds called labdanes were first identified in labdanum.[14] Some labdanes have antibacterial and antifungal activities.[15] Among the anticancer labdane-type compounds found in Cretan rockrose is sclareol. This has antileukaemic effects and activity against human breast cancer cell lines. It also enhances the activity of other anticancer drugs such as cisplatin and doxorubicin.[16]

**References:**

1. http://www.missouribotanicalgarden.org/PlantFinder/PlantFinderDetails.aspx?taxonid=279173 [Accessed 19.05.17]

2. http://www.plantlife.org.uk/uk/

**Ambergris**

discover-wild-plants-nature/plant-fungi-species/rock-rose [Accessed 19.05.17]

3. http://www.luontoportti.com/suomi/en/kukkakasvit/ common-rockrose [Accessed 19.05.17]

4. F. Mimms, (5th January 2008); Frost flowers; https://www.youtube.com/watch?v=HlXfaOFgkd4 [Accessed 19.05.17]

5. The Weather Channel, (10th October 2013); Strangest Weather On Earth: Rare Frost Flowers!; https://www.youtube.com/watch?v=mBnXHgAyaVg [Accessed 19.05.17]

6. J. Ouellette, (11th May 2012); From the Archives: Frost Flowers and Hot Capillary Action; Scientific American; https://blogs.scientificamerican.com/cocktail-party-physics/from-the-archives-frost-flowers-and-hot-capillary-action/ [Accessed 19.05.17]

7. Á. Rubio-Moraga, J. Argandoña, B. Mota, J. Pérez, A. Verde, J. Fajardo, J. Gómez Navarro, R. Castillo López, O. Ahrazem, L. Gómez-Gómez, (2013); Screening for polyphenols, antioxidant and antimicrobial activities of extracts from eleven *Helianthemum* taxa (Cistaceae) used in folk medicine in south-eastern Spain; *J. Ethnopharmacol.*, 148(1), 287–96; doi: 10.1016/j.jep.2013.04.028

8. http://www.bojensen.net/EssentialOilsEng/EssentialOils15/EssentialOils15.htm#Labdanum [Accessed 20.05.17]

9. http://www.bojensen.net/EssentialOilsEng/EssentialOils01/EssentiaOils01.htm#Amber [Accessed 20.05.17]

10. C. Graber, (26th April 2007); Strange but True: Whale Waste Is Extremely Valuable; Scientific American; https://www.scientificamerican.com/article/strange-but-true-whale-waste-is-valuable/ [Accessed 20.05.17]

11. S.A. Taha, M.W. Islam, A.M. Ageel, (1995); Effect of ambrein, a major constituent of ambergris,

on masculine sexual behavior in rats; *Arch. Int. Pharmacodyn. Ther.*, 329(2), 283–94; PMID: 8540767

12. M. Cross, (5th January 2016); Whale Poop in Perfume?; http://www.globalanimal.org/2016/01/05/whale-poop-in-perfume/ [Accessed 20.05.17]

13. Y.-Y. Gao, S. Tseng, (Granted 21st October 2014); Method for treating ocular demodex; *United States Patent* 8, 865, 232 B2; http://www.google.com/patents/US8865232 [Accessed 20.05.17]

14. J.D. Cocker, T.G. Halsall, (1956); 820. The chemistry of gum labdanum. Part II. The structure of labdanolic acid; *J. Chem. Soc.*, 4262–71; doi: 10.1039/JR9560004262

15. D. Papaefthimiou, A. Papanikolaou, V. Falara, S. Givanoudi, S. Kostas, A.K. Kanellis, (11th June 2014); Genus *Cistus*: a model for exploring labdane-type diterpenes' biosynthesis and a natural source of high value products with biological, aromatic, and pharmacological properties; *Front. Chem.*, 2, article 35; doi: 10.3389/fchem.2014.00035

16. K. Dimas, M. Papadaki, C. Tsimplouli, S. Hatziantoniou, K. Alevizopoulos, P. Pantazis, C. Demetzos, (2006); Labd-14-ene-8,13-diol (sclareol) induces cell cycle arrest and apoptosis in human breast cancer cells and enhances the activity of anticancer drugs; *Biomed. Pharmacother.*, 60(3), 127–33; doi: 10.1016/j.biopha.2006.01.003

# Water Violet

## (*Hottonia palustris*)

*Hottonia palustris* or water violet has finely divided leaves and is sometimes known as featherfoil or water yarrow. Linnaeus named the genus after a Dutch professor of medicine and botany at Leiden University, Petrus Hotton (sometimes written Peter Hotton or Petrus Houttuyn (1648–1709)). There are only two species in the genus – *Hottonia palustris*, native to Europe and parts of Asia and *Hottonia inflata*, native to North America. The American genus has markedly smaller flowers but thicker stems. The species name *palustris* refers to the plant's marshy or swampy habitat.

Water violet is an aquatic plant with submerged leaves. This has implications for its chemical defences. A study of the total phenolic content of 40 aquatic and semi-aquatic plants with floating, emergent or submerged leaves found that the total content was least in submerged leaves. Phenolics, including tannins, offer protection against pathogens, herbivores and UV-B radiation. Floating or emergent leaves are more vulnerable to attack as they are accessible to pathogens and herbivores from in and out of the water. Submerged leaves have a lower nitrogen content and a lower calorific value, making them less attractive to herbivores. And UV-B light penetrates water poorly so submerged leaves have less need for protection from this by phenolics. Plants with floating or emergent leaves need to invest more in their chemical protection.[1]

The presence of light and carbon dioxide is required for the synthesis of phenolics and other compounds

> **Water Violet** is the Bach flower remedy for those whose self-reliance and independence can make them feel cut off from others.

in plants. Both components are in limited supply beneath the water. To enable submerged leaves to obtain enough to provide energy, the leaves are thinner and finely divided (so have a larger surface area to volume ratio). They also lack cuticles so are relatively simple compared to floating or emergent leaves.

Aquatic plants can still obtain enough light to carry out photosynthesis, even when they have submerged leaves. However, suspended particles, dissolved substances and water depth can restrict the amount of light that penetrates the water.[2] As in non-aquatic plants, the light is harvested by chlorophyll in the leaves and provides energy to convert water and carbon dioxide ($CO_2$) to glucose and oxygen. As $CO_2$ diffuses through water 10,000 times more slowly than through air, it is beneficial to aquatic plants if their leaves are on or near the water surface.[3] Water violets are termed oxygenating plants. This means they get their nutrients from the water and release oxygen back into it. Therefore, they help maintain the ecological balance and prevent overgrowth of algae.[4]

The plants are an important source of oxygen for fish and invertebrates living in the water and if the quantity of light available is compromised (*e.g.* by cloudy weather or the introduction of certain light

**Submerged leaves**

blockers into the water) these may not survive. Fish kills are often the result of oxygen depletion, usually occurring overnight when levels reach a minimum.[5]

Water violets are vulnerable to the removal of their preferred habitat *e.g.* by increased urbanisation and in some places (*e.g.* Germany) they are considered to be endangered.[6] Other potential threats include water contamination and overgrowth of algae or other plants.[5] Bodies of water are sometimes treated with herbicides such as cyanatryn (no longer used in UK) to remove unwanted plant growth, but the effect on non-target plants such as water violets can also be significant.[7]

Water violets flower in May and June, producing white or pale violet flowers with yellow 'eyes'. The flowers are held above the water in whorls, one above the other on leafless stalks. Unlike many aquatic plants, they have five petals (rather than three). Flowers are hermaphroditic and come in two forms, or morphs, thrum and pin. The pin form has long pistils and short stamens whereas the thrum form has the reverse. Thus, the plant is termed heterostylous

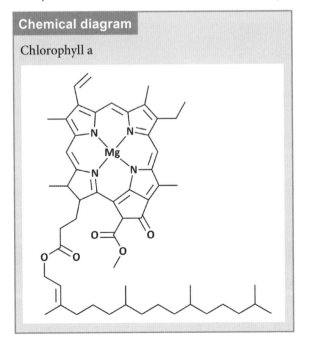

**Chemical diagram**

Chlorophyll a

(another difference between this species and *Hottonia inflata*). As these forms are determined by genes, all flowers on each individual plant are of the same type. Fertilisation usually occurs when pollen from one morph is transferred to the other morph (*i.e.* cross-pollination between morphs is favoured).[8] This is also a feature of primroses and was first described by Charles Darwin in 1862.[9]

## References:

1. A.J.P. Smolders, L.H.T. Vergeer, G. van der Velde and J.G.M. Roelofs, (2000); Phenolic contents of submerged, emergent and floating leaves of aquatic and semi-aquatic macrophyte species: why do they differ?; *Oikos*, 91(2), 307–10; doi: 10.1034/j.1600-0706.2000.910211.x

2. T. Lacoma, (24th April 2017); Photosynthesis in aquatic plants; http://sciencing.com/photosynthesis-aquatic-plants-5816031.html [Accessed 21.05.17]

3. D. Huebert, (29th October 1998); A basic Introduction to the physiology and ecology of aquatic plants; http://www.thekrib.com/Plants/phisio.html [Accessed 21.05.17]

4. https://www.velda.com/pond-maintenance/pond-plants/oxygenating-plants/ [Accessed 21.05.17]

5. University of Florida, Institute of Food and Agricultural Sciences; Dissolved Oxygen; http://plants.ifas.ufl.edu/manage/overview-of-florida-waters/water-quality/dissolved-oxygen/ [Accessed 21.05.17]

6. https://www.flowgrow.de/db/aquaticplants/hottonia-palustris [Accessed 21.05.17]

7. H.R.A. Scorgie, (1980); Ecological Effects of the Aquatic Herbicide Cyanatryn on a Drainage Channel; *J. Appl. Ecol.*, 17(1), 207–25; doi: 10.2307/2402976

8. http://www.habitas.org.uk/priority/species.asp?item=3932 [Accessed 21.05.17]

9. S. Shailes, (27th April 2013); The pin and thrum of primroses; https://plantscientist.wordpress.com/2013/04/27/organism-of-the-week-primrose-primula-vulgaris/ [Accessed 08.09.17]

# Rock Water

Rock Water is the only remedy not made from a plant but is included here for completeness. Water to make the remedy is taken from a healing spring. Any healing spring can be the source but it must be free from human interference so distant from areas of habitation. This will minimise any water pollution. Pollution of streams and springs has three major sources – fertilisers, pesticides and acid rain.[1]

Fertilisers are a source of the plant nutrients nitrogen and/or phosphorous and sometimes potassium. They promote growth and are used in agriculture. Common fertilisers are ammonium nitrate, potassium nitrate, urea and ammonium phosphate. These are water soluble so are readily washed into streams by rainwater.[2] This enrichment of nutrients in the water, called eutrophication, causes algae to grow, blocking sunlight from other aquatic plants. The plants die and along with the algae are decomposed by microbes. This depletes the oxygen levels in the water causing other organisms to die.[1,3]

Pesticides are used in agriculture to control animals or plants which adversely affect crops. One of the most commonly used classes is the pyrethrins, including pyrethrin I. The first examples were isolated from *Chrysanthemum cinerariifolium* and the compounds are potent insecticides.[1] Pesticides can be blown away from their target area or enter the water *via* run-off. Their toxicity is variable but pyrethrins are toxic to fish and other aquatic organisms as well as to bees.

Acid rain occurs when atmospheric pollutants, like nitrous oxide and sulfur dioxide from car exhausts,

**Rock Water** is the Bach flower remedy for rigidity and self-denial.

react with water to produce acids such as nitric acid and sulfuric acid. This increases the acidity of rain and of any body of water on which it falls.[1] As the acid rain causes the pH of water to fall (*i.e.* become more acidic), it may reach the critical point at which organisms cannot survive. This varies depending on the organism; for example, frogs can't survive in water below pH 4 but the mayflies they eat can't survive below pH 5.5.[4]

Water pollution can be more problematic when wastewater enters rivers. Some recent studies have highlighted the effects of commonly-used prescription medications which can contaminate water. Among the biggest polluters are the benzodiazepines like Valium and oxazepam. The latter compound has been found in Swedish rivers and makes fish less fearful and more active. These drugs have also been found to be persistent in the environment. Oxazepam from the early 1970s can be identified in river sediment with almost no degradation. And even today, water treatment plants don't attempt to remove it.[5]

**Chemical diagram**

Pyrethrin I

**Chemical diagram**

Oxazepam

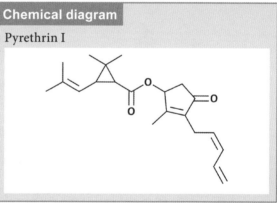

Antidepressants like sertraline (Zoloft) also have an effect on fish, suppressing territorial aggression and promoting sociability and boldness. However, although in a laboratory environment these effects are beneficial and the fish live longer and perhaps happier lives, in the real world, changes of behaviour which make fish more relaxed and bolder may make them more likely to be eaten.[5]

Other effects of drugs including Prozac (fluoxetine) have been observed in starlings. Prozac causes changes in their feeding patterns and females show a reduced libido which, in the long term, could affect the viability of the species. There are various possible solutions to pharmaceutical pollution including filtration of wastewater through constructed wetlands but their high cost raises the question of who should pay. Is it the pharmaceutical industry, the water companies or the consumers who directly or indirectly cause the drugs or their metabolites to enter the water?[5]

### References:

1. BBC Bitesize; Water Pollution; http://www.bbc.co.uk/schools/gcsebitesize/science/edexcel/problems_in_environment/pollutionrev3.shtml [Accessed 29.05.17]

2. BBC Bitesize; Fertilisers and Crop Yield; http://www.bbc.co.uk/schools/gcsebitesize/science/add_gateway_pre_2011/chemical/fertilisersrev1.shtml [Accessed 29.05.17]

3. BBC Bitesize; Eutrophication; http://www.bbc.co.uk/schools/gcsebitesize/science/edexcel/problems_in_environment/pollutionrev4.shtml [Accessed 29.05.17]

4. https://www.epa.gov/acidrain/effects-acid-rain [Accessed 09.10.17]

5. I.E. Steinmark, (2017); Fish on Drugs; *Chemistry World*, 14(4), 48–51; (online version, Fish on Valium; https://www.chemistryworld.com/feature/antidepressant-pollution/2500495.article)

# Photo Credits

**Cover** ©Storyblocks

**Cover inset** Tracey van den Ban

**Kate Lennard-Jones**
p iv(top)

**Frauke Möschler**
p viii

**Shutterstock**
pp 1 ©Andrew Darby Photography, 17(middle) ©btwcapture, 19 ©Iva Vagnerova, 27(left) ©Alin Brotea, 38(bottom) ©dinkaspell, 45 ©Manfred Ruckszio, 66(bottom) ©Gertjan Hooijer, 86 ©bbearlyam, 98(top) ©Anton Kozyrev, 108 ©pokku, 116 ©Charlotte Erpenbeck, 119 ©ah_photobox, 121 ©Zhukovskaya Elena, 125 ©LutsenkoLarissa, 133 ©Richard Pinder, 136 ©PFMphotostock, 141(left) ©Jamie Farrant, 142 ©Neil Hardwick

**Gwenda Kyd**
pp 2, 3(top), 8(left), 10, 11, 12(right), 17(top), 17(bottom), 21(left), 27(right), 42(top), 49(left), 64(top), 100(top), 100(bottom), 145(left)

**Wikimedia Commons (used under various licences, details on request)**
pp 3(bottom) ©Dcrjscr, 8(right) ©WPF, 9 ©Geoff Wong, 15(top) ©Frank Vincentz, 20 ©Tamorlan, 21(right) ©Benjamin Gimmel, 23 ©H. Zell, 30(top) ©Jörg Hempel, 33 ©Rosser1954, 53 ©Dazzii, 59(bottom) ©Charles de Mille-Isles, 64(bottom) ©Frank Vincentz, 68(top) ©Melburnian, 68(bottom) ©Ronnie Nijboer – Nijboer Collection, 73 ©Christian Fischer, 76 ©Leo Michels, 77(top) ©Accipiter (R. Altenkamp, Berlin), 77(bottom) ©Dominique Jacquin, 79(top) ©Petr Filippov, 80(right) ©Bildoj, 87(right) ©H. Zell, 88(left) ©H. Zell, 88(right, top) ©H. Zell, ©88(right, bottom) Malte, 90(right) ©Christian Fischer, 94(right) ©Didier Descouens, 95 ©O. Pichard, 97 ©O. Pichard, 103 ©Xemenendura, 122(right) ©3268zauber, 123 ©Quert1234, 124 ©Meneerke

bloem, 129 ©Stefan.lefnacr, 130 ©H. Zell, 131(left) ©Walter Seigmund, 131(right) ©H. Zell, 132(bottom) ©Algirdas, 134 ©Losch, 137(right) ©Wouter Hagens, 138(left) ©Daderot, 138(right) ©Wouter Hagens, 141(right) ©Der Michels (www.imagines-plantarum.de), 143(left) ©crockodile from Austin, TX, 143(right) ©Enrico Blasutto, 144 ©Peter Kaminski, 145(right) ©Thommybe, 146 ©Aiwok, 147 ©Christian Fischer, 148(upper) ©Christian Fischer, 148 (bottom) ©Christian Fischer

**Nicola Hanefeld**
pp iv(bottom), 4, 12(left), 22(bottom), 48(bottom), 58(bottom), 63(right), 79(bottom), 110(right)

**Mo Sibbons**
pp 5, 13, 26(right), 62, 83(left), 83(right)

**Pixabay**
pp v(left), v(right), vi, vii, 6, 7, 14, 15(bottom), 16, 18, 22(top), 24, 25(bottom), 26 (left), 28(left), 28(right), 29, 30(bottom), 31, 32(left), 32(right), 34, 35, 36, 37, 38(top), 39, 40, 41, 42(middle), 43, 44, 46, 47, 48(top), 49(right), 50, 51, 52(left), 52(right), 54(top), 54(bottom), 55, 56, 57(left), 57(right), 58(middle), 59(top), 60, 61, 65, 66(top), 67, 69, 70, 71(right), 71(bottom), 72, 75(left), 75(right), 78, 80(left), 81, 82, 84, 87(left), 89, 90(left), 91, 94(bottom), 101, 102, 104, 105, 106(left), 106(right), 107(left), 107(right), 109, 110(left), 111, 112, 113, 114, 115, 117, 118(left), 118(right), 120, 126, 127, 128, 132(top), 135, 137(left), 149, 150, 151(top), 151(bottom)

**Public Domain via Wikimedia Commons**
pp 25(top), 63(left) Bryson Jack, 85 AnRo0002 92 Javier Martin, 122(left) Pipi69e, 139 AnRo0002, 140 Brodero Matthisen

**Heathergems.com**
pp 74(left, upper), 74(left, lower)

**Flickr**
pp 93 Donald Macauley, 96 Donald Macauley, 98(bottom) "pastilletes"/Joan Simon, Barcelona, España, 99 "pastilletes"/Joan Simon, Barcelona, España